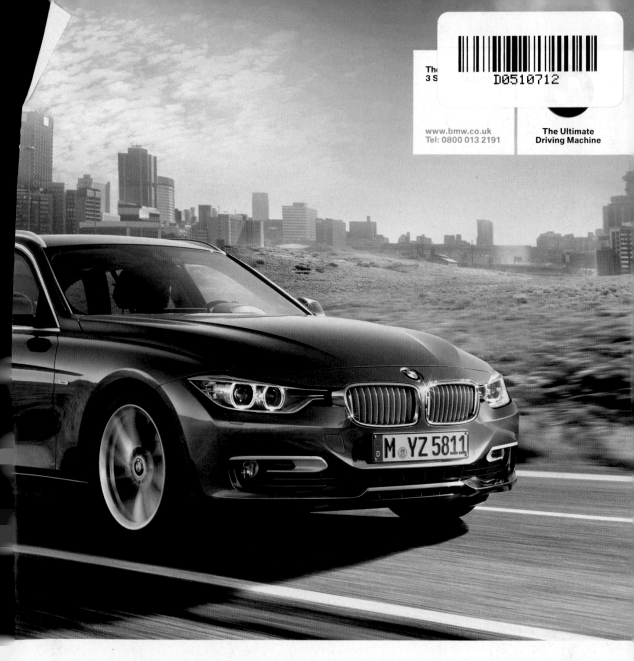

FRONTIER.

72.4 mpg (5.5 – 3.9 ltr/100 km). Combined 41.5 – 60.1 mpg (6.8 – 4.7 ltr/100 km). CO₂ emissions 159 – 123 g/km.
velopments and is standard across the model range.

OYSTER PERPETUAL EXPLORER II

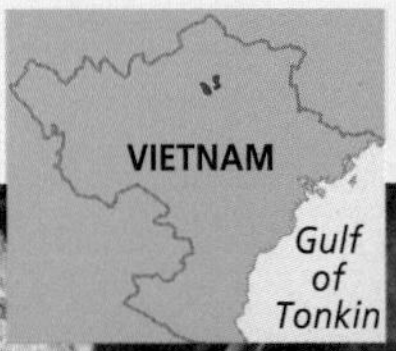

Tonkin Snub-nosed Monkey *(Rhinopithecus avunculus)*
Size: Head and body length, 50 - 65 cm; tail, 65 - 92 cm **Weight:** Males approx. 14 kg; females approx. 8.5 kg **Habitat:** Lowland tropical broadleaf monsoon forests in montane limestone formations
Surviving number: Estimated at 260

VIETNAM

Gulf of Tonkin

Photographed by Quyet Le Khac

WILDLIFE AS CANON SEES IT

Phantom of the forest. Once presumed extinct, the Tonkin snub-nosed monkey reappeared in 1989 like a ghost from the past and today clings to a precarious existence in a few isolated locations. Large, semi-cohesive bands of 25-80 individuals are organized around family groups, all ranging and resting together. Active during the day, they move through the trees searching out edible leaves, fruits and seeds. When hunted, bands split into smaller units. But with their habitat being lost or disturbed at an alarming rate, it's becoming harder and harder to vanish into the forest and leave the hunters behind.

As we see it, we can help make the world a better place. Raising awareness of endangered species is just one of the ways we at Canon are taking action—for the good of the planet we call home. Visit **canon.com/environment** to learn more.

Canon

VOL. 222 • NO. 5
NOVEMBER 2012

NATIONAL GEOGRAPHIC

*"I spotted a pair of women's
shoes on a porch...covered
in ruby red glitter."*
page 133

60

FEATURES

On the Cover
Map by Jeremy Collins
Cheetah photo by Ken Geiger, NGM Staff

DEPARTMENTS

FOR SUBSCRIPTIONS, GIFT MEMBERSHIPS,
OR CHANGES OF ADDRESS, CONTACT CUSTOMER
SERVICE AT *NGMSERVICE.COM* OR CALL
1-800-NGS-LINE (647-5463). OUTSIDE THE U.S.
AND CANADA PLEASE CALL +1-813-979-6845.

 Please recycle.

Fast-Forward and Replay

I first saw the explosion of speed on the Serengeti Plain 24 years ago. With astonishing swiftness, the cheetah closed the gap between predator and prey, then lay beside the struggling Thomson's gazelle with her jaws around his throat. I wanted a slow-motion replay to document that speed.

Thirteen years later I tried for one on a grassy flat in Namibia. Laurie Marker of the Cheetah Conservation Fund had raised a cheetah she'd named Chewbaaka. To keep him fit, she'd trained him to chase a lure. Photo engineer Kenji Yamaguchi and I set up a dozen cameras programmed to fire eight frames a second in sequence. For more than a week Chewbaaka chased the lure. The results were disappointing. The cat did his job, but we didn't have the technology to do ours. This summer, with the help of National Geographic's Big Cats Initiative and Darlene and Jeff Anderson, we tried again. The Cincinnati Zoo offered its cheetahs, and cheetah guru Cathyrn Hilker offered her expertise. A crew of Hollywood's best set up a 400-foot-long track with a remote-control sled to keep pace with each cat. On the sled were a high-def digital cinema camera firing off 1,200 frames a second and three cameras shooting 42 frames a second in sequence. A 150,000-watt light illuminated the course. For three days the cheetahs did their job, but the results fell short of expectations. Finally, the last night, everything clicked. In this month's issue and on our app, you'll see these images of the fastest runner on Earth, inspired by a Serengeti cheetah 24 years ago.

Cincinnati Zoo cheetah Tommy T—a young male— takes a nighttime run.

Easter Island

If the *moai* could talk, they would probably talk about one of the most important guys on any construction team after ▶ the foreman: the halfway-intelligent lazy guy. After all the dragging, walking, skidding, and all the broken statues lying by the wayside, this guy would figure out an easier way. He would have seen they were on a hillside, so why not cut them into round cylinders and roll them down the hillside. Then the problem goes from moving them to just stopping them. And the carving guys could have finished them in place.

JOE RIP
Bellingham, Washington

Last year we were on a cruise ship that stopped at Easter Island but couldn't land its passengers because the waves were too high. We could see many buses lined up at the harbor and estimated that the local tourist industry lost significant revenue that morning alone. We were told by the crew that this happened more often than not. They rated the chance of getting ashore from a cruise ship as low as one in four. The Chilean government needs to upgrade the harbor to increase tourist dollars not only to support the local economy but also to have more funds to preserve the monuments.

DAVID AND SUSAN JACKSON
Dundas, Ontario

Unmentioned in your article is the invasion of non-native plants that are overrunning the land except in parklands managed for tourism. When this is coupled with the overpopulation of horses, the future of Easter Island is not encouraging. Will this be yet another "ecological catastrophe" for this island?

LINDA C. CORK
Palo Alto, California

The unanswered question is: How did the Rapanui stand the moai upright? They would have little problem rolling the moai to their assigned beaches. But without shipboard rigging, they would not be able to right the toppled ones. Once they got to the beach, the moai could have been tilted over a small cliff, then "walked" into position.

ROBERT HOUSTON
Torrance, California

Corrections

JULY 2012: EASTER ISLAND Page 39: Pavel Pavel's 1986 statue-moving experiment did not damage the moai's base. Damage occurred in his 1987 experiment with a replica.
VANISHING VOICES Page 70: *Tradzy* necklaces are worth up to seven mithan (Himalayan cattle), not two.
RUSSIAN SUMMER Pages 124, 128: Raisa Stepanov should read Raisa Stepanova and *biali* should read *beliy*.

FEEDBACK *Some readers offered their thoughts on how the* moai *were moved.*

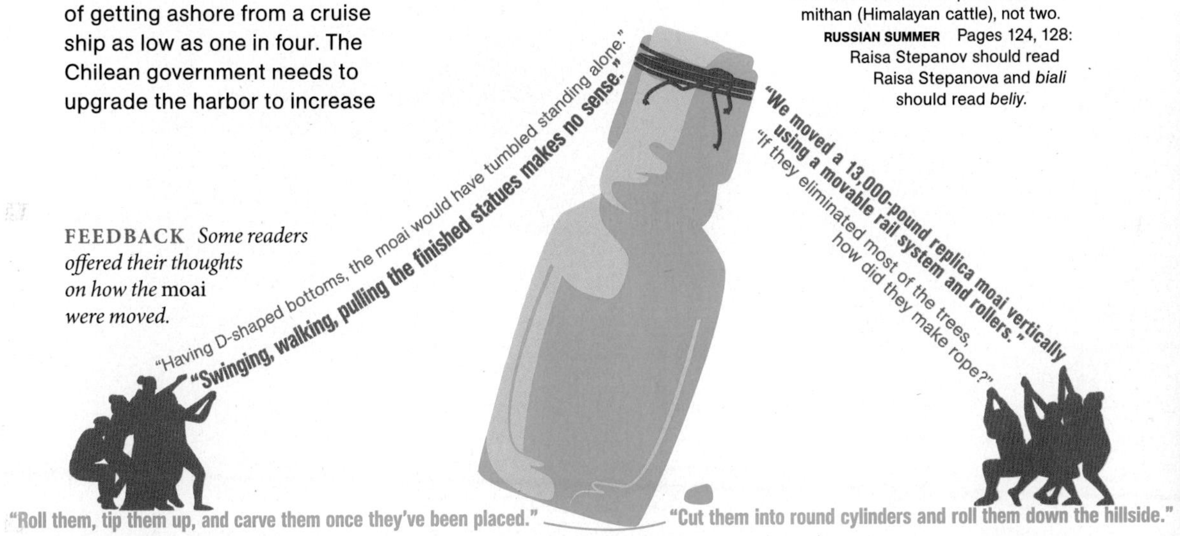

"Having D-shaped bottoms, the moai would have tumbled standing alone."

"**Swinging, walking, pulling the finished statues makes no sense.**"

"**We moved a 13,000-pound replica moai vertically using a movable rail system and rollers.**"

"If they eliminated most of the trees, how did they make rope?"

"Roll them, tip them up, and carve them once they've been placed."

"Cut them into round cylinders and roll them down the hillside."

EMAIL ngsforum@ngm.com **TWITTER** @NatGeoMag **WRITE** National Geographic Magazine, PO Box 98199, Washington, DC 20090-8199. Include name, address, and daytime telephone. Letters may be edited for clarity and length.

GRAPHIC: JOSHUA MAXWELL

The Earth's growing population and limited resources mean that innovative ideas are critical to create solutions for energy conservation, generation, and distribution. National Geographic, in partnership with Shell, launched **The Great Energy Challenge** to explore these issues and provide a forum where innovation can be showcased and shared. Go to **GreatEnergyChallenge.com** to join the conversation.

A WORLD OF INNOVATION:
Energy Ideas Around the Globe

ENERGY NEWS **AND ENERGY BLOGS**

Stay updated on the future of fuel and power with **Energy News** and **Energy Blogs** written by experts. Check out these stories below from around the world, and add your voice to discussion threads.

Turning Torso in Western Harbour, Malmö, Sweden

Formula One Legend Sets Course for Energy-Efficient Car Design

SHALFORD, ENGLAND

Europe's First Carbon-Neutral Neighborhood

MALMÖ, SWEDEN

India Power Outage Spotlights Energy Planning Failure

MUMBAI, INDIA

NEW ORLEANS, LA

A $200,000 Green Home Designed by Frank Gehry

CENTRAL UGANDA

Low-Cost Solar Brightens Lives in Developing World

SINGAPORE

Singapore's "Zero Energy Building" is a Test Bed for Green Building Innovations

THE GREAT ENERGY CHALLENGE **GRANTEE SPOTLIGHT**

EARTHSPARK INTERNATIONAL IN HAITI. Seventy percent of Haitian households currently lack access to grid electricity. The Great Energy Challenge grantee EarthSpark International is launching Haiti's first pre-pay micro-grid that will provide affordable, reliable, and sustainable electricity to 40 paying customers. The grid will be scalable to serve all of downtown Les Anglais and to interconnect with any grid extension that ultimately reaches the area. Moreover, the grid will be replicable: within five years, hundreds of small towns could gain access to locally generated power.

NATIONAL GEOGRAPHIC

Be a part of the solution; take part in the challenge.
Go to **GREATENERGYCHALLENGE.COM** to learn more about and contribute to the world's energy solutions.

A NATIONAL GEOGRAPHIC INITIATIVE IN PARTNERSHIP WITH SHELL

Vanishing Voices

Russ Rymer has fallen prey to a romanticized fallacy of languages, and the Inuit having dozens of words for snow is the most common example. Rymer says that the Todzhu reindeer herders "have an elaborate vocabulary for reindeer; an *iyi düktüg myiys*, for example, is a castrated former stud in its fourth year." English also has a vocabulary for such a reindeer: "a castrated former stud in its fourth year." And English also has dozens of words for snow: "ice, sleet, snow, hail, frost, slush, glaciers, snowflakes…"

JULIUS YANG
Los Angeles, California

What an astonishing philosophical insight into the Tuvan language: Their word for "going back" also means the future—to go forward means the past. We are truly walking backward

Many of the 7,000 languages will go, but ones that meet the people's needs will remain.

in life. All we can see is the past, and try as we may, we cannot look over our shoulder into the future.

KIRSI RAJAPURO
County Wicklow, Ireland

I am concerned that the French language is not listed in the ten dominant languages. It is estimated that about 300 million people regularly speak French—in Quebec, North and West Africa, parts of Belgium and Switzerland, and France. It is therefore far ahead of German, Japanese, and Portuguese.

HERVE PLUSQUELLEC
Washington, D.C.

The ranking considers first-language users only, not all those who can speak a language. By this measure, French counts 67.8 million people in 60 countries—a ranking of 16th.

At the American Museum of Natural History looking at Cro-Magnon and Neanderthal peoples, my friend remarked, "They've gone on before us." The word "before" struck me—its ambivalence between in the past and the implication in front of us. I've never thought of time in the same way since.

JIM LOWE
Elizaville, New York

"Vanishing Voices" misses the point entirely. Language is not a jewel to be cherished. It is a tool, and when it no longer supports the needs of the populace, it should be thrown in the garbage like other worn-out tools. The English language evolved because the island nation had to trade with the Continent. The English developed a multiplicity of tenses to support that trade. Language must change to meet needs. Many of the 7,000 languages will go, but ones that meet the people's needs will remain.

DONALD E. OLANDER
Phoenix, Arizona

Epic Storms

Can it really be said that "a storm giveth…wind to inert turbines"? More accurately, the turbines shut down during severe storms, so the blades do not overrotate or the towers collapse.

PAT HENRY
East Longmeadow, Massachusetts

NEXT: Cursive

I'm a sophomore and one of four students in my grade who know how to write cursive and one of two who actually use it. In my papa's day cursive was a mark of education; print would always be trumped by even badly executed cursive on a job application. Now the applications prohibit cursive. Many teachers at our school discourage cursive because they can't read it. Perhaps it isn't the computers that push out these marks of the pen; perhaps it is our culture.

MARLEE BALDRIDGE
Harrisburg, Missouri

FLASHBACK:
Smoke Signals

I was interested to read that "Dixon was adopted by the Wolf clan of the Mohawk Nation and given the name of Ka-ra-Kon-tie, or Flying Sun." If my limited knowledge of the language is correct, Ka Ra Kontie in ancient Egyptian means "true flying spirit of the Sun." Coincidence?

DAVID GIRLING
Kent, England

Egyptologist Günter Dreyer notes that Ka Ra could be translated as "soul/spirit/essence of the sun" and occurs in several royal names. The overlap is coincidental.

Leverage from
the EU
2007—2013

European Union
European Regional Development Fund

No ordinary Night Sky

OnlyInLapland.com

LAPLIFY
YOUR
LIFE

Available on the
App Store

Experience the Northern Lights here and now.
Download free, *augmented reality* Laplication.

Lapland —
The North of
Finland

DISCOVER THE ULTIMATE G&T EXPERIENCE

INFUSED WITH *Imagination*

VISIONS

Saudi Arabia.
Flooded with light as dusk signals the near end of daylong fasting, Mecca's Great Mosque brims with Muslims performing the *umrah* pilgrimage during Ramadan. As with the sacred hajj, they circle around the cube-shaped Kaaba, Islam's holiest site.

Spain
Heat engulfs a horse—dampened to prevent burning—as it races through a bonfire during Las Luminarias de San Antón in San Bartolomé de Pinares. The ritual, held the night before a festival for blessing animals, is thought to purify horses.

Romania
On a rural stretch near
Odobeşti, a teenager
sets off at dawn to saw
logs at the homes and
farms of local residents.
Wintertime brings
demand in the area
for woodcutters' help
in preparing fuel for
heating and cooking.

PHOTO: TAMAS DEZSO

EDITORS' CHOICE **Cesar Aristeiguieta** Santa Monica, California

Watching captive wolves on a ranch in Kalispell, Montana, Aristeiguieta witnessed a young male (left) challenge the alpha male. "Despite tense and dangerous moments, the handlers were able to separate them," reports the photographer, 51, who's also a physician.

READERS' CHOICE

Colleen Pinski
Peyton, Colorado

Pinski, 28, and her husband drove several hundred miles to Albuquerque just to get a better view of an annular solar eclipse. "We're avid adventurists, so we couldn't pass up the opportunity," she says. A supertelephoto lens helped secure a larger-than-life image.

We create chemistry
that helps skin love the sun.

To keep your skin healthy and protected, even on the sunniest days, you need the right combination of UV filters. Sunscreens and daily care products containing UV filters from our Tinosorb®, Uvinul® and Z-COTE® product ranges cover both the UVA and the UVB spectrum. They absorb the harmful UV rays and turn them into harmless heat. When sunny days can be enjoyed all summer long, it's because at BASF, we create chemistry.

www.wecreatechemistry.com

The Chemical Company

Mighty Moringa

"Mother's best friend," "never die," "drumstick tree"—moringa takes many names around the world. For centuries a traditional remedy for skin, respiratory, digestive, and other ailments, it's now being hailed as a way to battle famine and malnutrition. With vitamin-and-mineral-packed leaves, the drought-resistant tree also grows fast—up to 12 feet in a season.

From spicy seeds to bitter leaves (often ground into a powder), most of *Moringa oleifera* can be eaten or used, says Jed Fahey of Johns Hopkins. Its seeds, crushed, can even help purify water. Although animal studies support anecdotal evidence of its medicinal benefits, more human trials are needed, Fahey notes. Meanwhile, the "miracle tree" is catching on in impoverished areas of Africa, Asia, and Latin America, entering local dishes and lore. —*Luna Shyr*

A native of the Indian subcontinent, the moringa tree has highly nutritious leaves, shaped here from dried leaf powder.

Gram for gram, dried moringa leaves have

25 × iron in spinach
17 × calcium in milk
15 × potassium in bananas
10 × vitamin A in carrots
 9 × protein in yogurt

ART: JENNA TURNER, NGM STAFF. PHOTO: REBECCA HALE, NGM STAFF
CHART SOURCE: LOWELL FUGLIE, *THE MIRACLE TREE: MORINGA OLEIFERA*

PRODUCED BY YOU. DIRECTED BY YOU. CREATED BY YOU. WRITTEN BY YOU. COSTUME DESIGN BY YOU.
ART DIRECTION BY YOU. EDITED BY YOU. SOUNDTRACK BY YOU. CASTING BY YOU.

PERU
EMPIRE·OF
HIDDEN·TREASURES

THE UNTOUCHED
PRE-INCA REMAINS OF
AN ANCESTRAL CULTURE!

SIPÁN - LAMBAYEQUE

DON'T WATCH
THE MOVIE.
LIVE IT FOR REAL!

VISIT PERU
www.peru.travel

NEXT

An average forest stores about 100,000 tons of carbon per square mile. Sea grass meadows can hold nearly triple that.

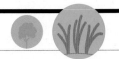

Horse Power

Diminutive konik horses stand about four feet tall, but they can have a big impact on biodiversity. By eating the woody vegetation that overcomes open marshes, these likely descendants of the horses in prehistoric cave paintings are helping revive the natural landscape that existed when large herbivores roamed freely.

Before Neolithic farmers began to till marshes in what is now Europe, grazers kept forests from creeping in, which allowed varied habitats for birds, insects, and plants to flourish. Today conservationists are trying to revive that diversity. In many places that means cutting brush back with chain saws. But koniks are cheaper and better at it. The horses are now at work in nearly a dozen countries—including some 20 sites in the U.K. alone. —*A. R. Williams*

Leeches Locate Elusive Species

Scientists are out for blood in Vietnam. DNA in the blood meal of 14 of 25 leeches came from hard-to-track tropical forest species like the serow—helping biologists monitor mammal diversity (and maybe endangered species) in inaccessible terrain. —*Lacey Gray*

One leech

No DNA detected Serow Truong Son muntjac Annamite striped rabbit Small-toothed ferret-badger Cow Pig

Near-threatened species in decline

Currently listed as "data deficient"

First confirmed record for Bach Ma National Park

Domesticated species

PHOTO: JIM BRANDENBURG, MINDEN PICTURES. GRAPHICS: ÁLVARO VALIÑO (TOP); LAWSON PARKER, NGM STAFF. SOURCE: TOM GILBERT, NATURAL HISTORY MUSEUM OF DENMARK

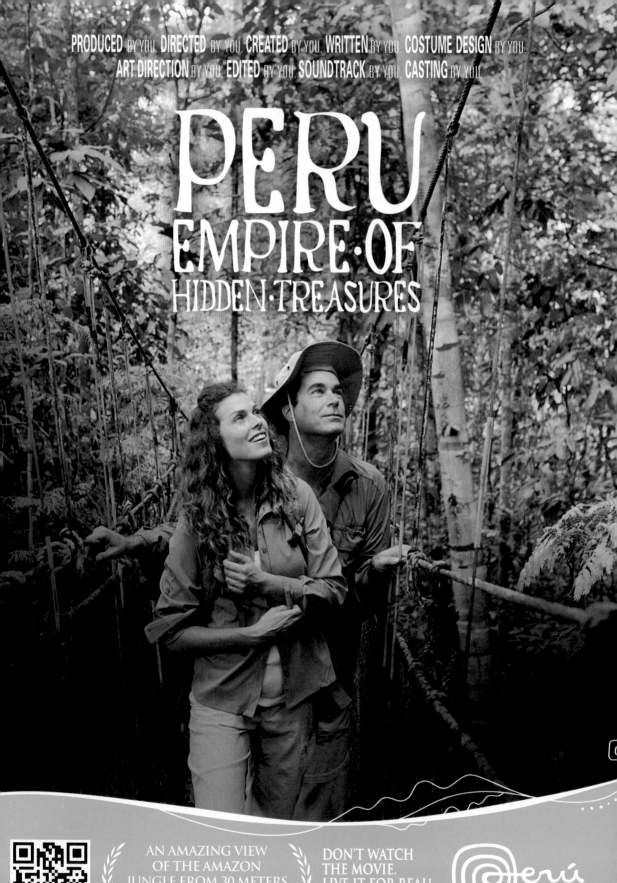

PRODUCED BY YOU. DIRECTED BY YOU. CREATED BY YOU. WRITTEN BY YOU. COSTUME DESIGN BY YOU.
ART DIRECTION BY YOU. EDITED BY YOU. SOUNDTRACK BY YOU. CASTING BY YOU.

PERU
EMPIRE·OF
HIDDEN·TREASURES

AN AMAZING VIEW
OF THE AMAZON
JUNGLE FROM 30 METERS
UP IN THE AIR

CANOPY - LORETO

DON'T WATCH
THE MOVIE.
LIVE IT FOR REAL!

VISIT PERU
www.peru.travel

Mobile cellular subscriptions per person
Top five countries or territories per continent by year

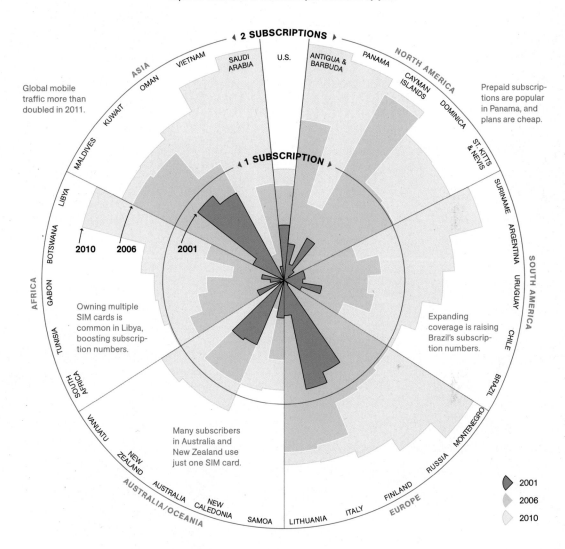

2 SUBSCRIPTIONS

NORTH AMERICA

ASIA

VIETNAM · SAUDI ARABIA · U.S. · ANTIGUA & BARBUDA · PANAMA

OMAN

CAYMAN ISLANDS

KUWAIT

DOMINICA

Global mobile traffic more than doubled in 2011.

Prepaid subscriptions are popular in Panama, and plans are cheap.

MALDIVES

ST. KITTS & NEVIS

1 SUBSCRIPTION

LIBYA

SURINAME

BOTSWANA

SOUTH AMERICA

ARGENTINA

2010   2006   2001

GABON

URUGUAY

AFRICA

Owning multiple SIM cards is common in Libya, boosting subscription numbers.

Expanding coverage is raising Brazil's subscription numbers.

TUNISIA

CHILE

SOUTH AFRICA

BRAZIL

VANUATU

NEW ZEALAND

Many subscribers in Australia and New Zealand use just one SIM card.

MONTENEGRO

AUSTRALIA/OCEANIA

AUSTRALIA

RUSSIA

NEW CALEDONIA

SAMOA · LITHUANIA · ITALY · FINLAND

FINLAND

EUROPE

🔴 2001
🔵 2006
⚪ 2010

Mobilizing Nations

That gap at 12 o'clock (above) is no mistake. The U.S., where most cell phone plans are postpaid, lags much of the world in mobile subscriptions per person. Subscription rates skew higher where prepaid plans are the norm, because consumers can swap numerous SIM cards—portable memory chips—in and out of one phone to get the best rates for calling, texting, and Internet access. Numbers are often higher in developing nations where landlines are scarce or expensive, says statistician Esperanza Magpantay. Any subscription generating traffic within three months counts as active, she says. Cisco projects the number of mobile devices will top the world's population this year. *—John Briley*

JASON TREAT, NGM STAFF. SOURCES: INTERNATIONAL TELECOMMUNICATION UNION; WORLD TELECOMMUNICATION/ICT DEVELOPMENT REPORT AND DATABASE; WORLD BANK

British passion.
Powered by Norwegian gas.

From lighting stadiums and heating homes, to powering our industry.
Natural gas is the most versatile fossil fuel and can meet the UK's energy
needs in a reliable, cost-efficient way. Norwegian gas is available today.
Be enlightened at goodideas.statoil.com.

Statoil

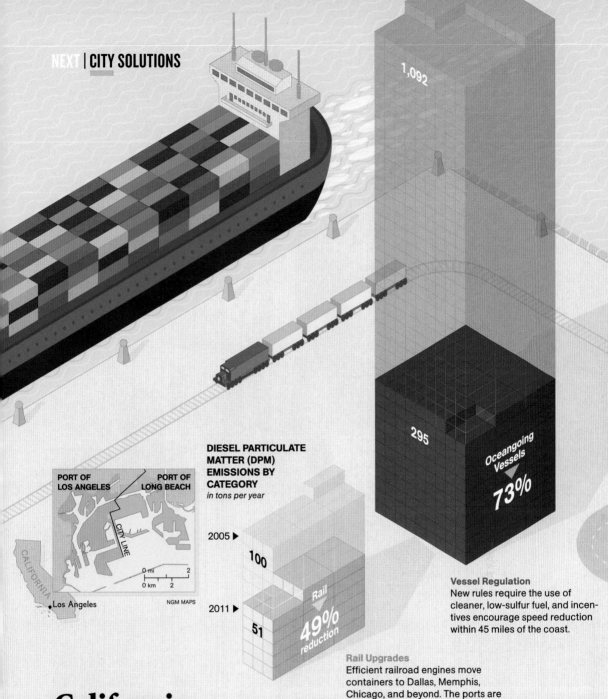

1,092

295

Oceangoing
Vessels

73%

**DIESEL PARTICULATE
MATTER (DPM)
EMISSIONS BY
CATEGORY**
in tons per year

PORT OF
LOS ANGELES

PORT OF
LONG BEACH

CITY LINE

0 mi 2
0 km 2

CALIFORNIA

•Los Angeles

NGM MAPS

2005 ▶

100

Rail

2011 ▶

51

49%
reduction

Vessel Regulation
New rules require the use of
cleaner, low-sulfur fuel, and incen-
tives encourage speed reduction
within 45 miles of the coast.

Rail Upgrades
Efficient railroad engines move
containers to Dallas, Memphis,
Chicago, and beyond. The ports are
also considering a maglev system.

California
Ports Go Green

If anything for sale in the U.S. says "Made in China"—furniture, sneakers, auto parts—the
odds are fifty-fifty it came through the Port of Los Angeles or the adjacent Port of Long
Beach. In 2011 cranes off-loaded nearly 14 million shipping containers holding more than
300 billion pounds of goods (not just from China) and about 14 billion gallons of fuel.

Together L.A. and Long Beach form the largest port in the Western Hemisphere, a nearly
24-square-mile complex of ships, docks, cranes, roads, trucks, and trains so massive it has
its own AAA map. Greening it was an equally large undertaking. Replacing machinery,
fuels, and infrastructure has reduced harmful pollutants by more than 27,000 tons, and
today the port's cleaned-up waters attract sea lions, pelicans, and sharks. —*David Helvarg*

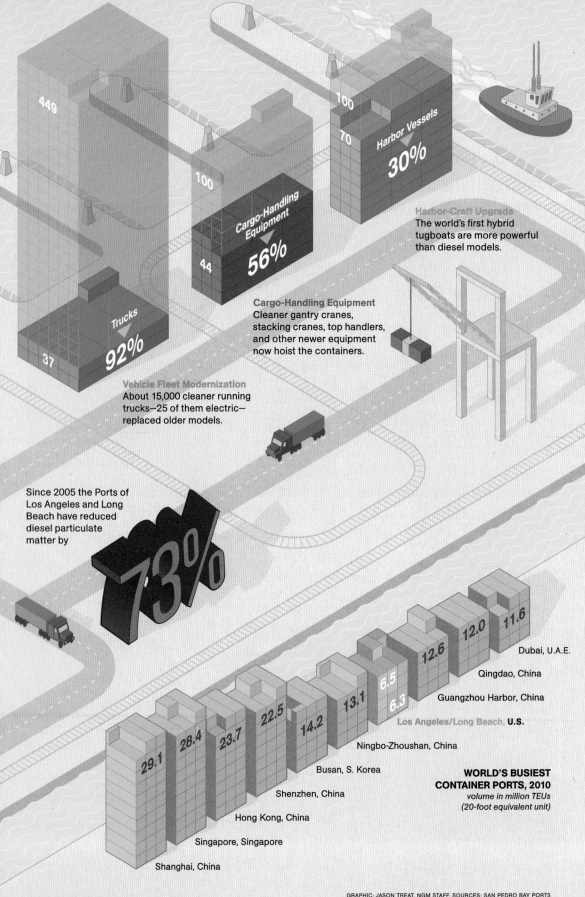

449

100

Harbor Vessels

100
70

30%

Cargo-Handling
Equipment

44

56%

Harbor-Craft Upgrade
The world's first hybrid
tugboats are more powerful
than diesel models.

Trucks

37

92%

Cargo-Handling Equipment
Cleaner gantry cranes,
stacking cranes, top handlers,
and other newer equipment
now hoist the containers.

Vehicle Fleet Modernization
About 15,000 cleaner running
trucks—25 of them electric—
replaced older models.

Since 2005 the Ports of
Los Angeles and Long
Beach have reduced
diesel particulate
matter by

73%

11.6 Dubai, U.A.E.

12.0 Qingdao, China

12.6 Guangzhou Harbor, China

6.5
6.3 Los Angeles/Long Beach, **U.S.**

13.1 Ningbo-Zhoushan, China

14.2 Busan, S. Korea

22.5 Shenzhen, China

23.7 Hong Kong, China

28.4 Singapore, Singapore

29.1 Shanghai, China

**WORLD'S BUSIEST
CONTAINER PORTS, 2010**
*volume in million TEUs
(20-foot equivalent unit)*

GRAPHIC: JASON TREAT, NGM STAFF. SOURCES: SAN PEDRO BAY PORTS
CLEAN AIR ACTION PLAN; PORT OF LOS ANGELES; PORT OF LONG BEACH

Human figures about eight inches tall mark an ancient Mexican site likely used by healers.

Mystical Rock Art

Amid the arid mountains of central Mexico, an archaeological survey in the state of Guanajuato has identified almost 50 rock art sites encompassing more than 5,000 separate images. Carlos Viramontes Anzures and Luz María Flores of the National Institute of Anthropology and History last year discovered a few sites painted as early as the first century, and some from as late as the 1900s. Most date from roughly A.D. 1000 to 1500 and were painted by hunter-gatherers who used mineral-based colors to depict humans, animals, and abstract shapes.

Such paintings were created in sacred spaces used for healing rituals, rites of passage, and petitions for rain, Viramontes Anzures believes. One small valley alone holds 29 of the sites. "That's an unusual concentration," he says. "It must have been a very special place." So far, though, the reason remains a mystery. —A. R. Williams

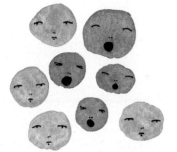

YOU ARE GETTING SLEEPY Or are you? New research suggests yawning doesn't just signal fatigue; it's linked to empathy too. Italian anthropologists Elisabetta Palagi and Ivan Norscia spent a year stealthily observing people as they opened wide in public and family settings. The two also noted when others nearby followed suit. Called "yawn contagion," the phenomenon occurred often among relatives, rarely among strangers. Age and sex didn't make a difference, indicating the behavior is emotionally driven. Consider it a facial act of love. —Catherine Zuckerman

PHOTO: CARLOS VIRAMONTES ANZURES, INAH. NGM MAPS. ART: MARC JOHNS

NEXT

An average person walks about 100,000 miles in a lifetime—
the equivalent of circling the Earth four times.

Cold Case

Anyone who's ever chugged a chilly drink or eaten ice cream too quickly has felt it: the excruciating pain behind the temples and forehead known as brain freeze. The short-lived condition has long been labeled a physiological mystery. Now research suggests a change in blood flow may be what brings on the icy throb—and perhaps migraines too.

Intrigued by the high rate of chronic headaches he observed at the War Related Illness and Injury Study Center, scientist Jorge Serrador decided to test their origins. The onset of headaches can't be predicted, and he didn't want to prompt them with drugs. So Serrador examined easy-to-induce brain freeze by having participants gulp ice water through a straw aimed at the roof of the mouth. Using a Doppler monitor, Serrador found that just before pain arose, blood flow surged in an artery that feeds the front of the brain. The rush creates pressure in the skull—bringing on the brain freeze. When the artery shrinks back, possibly as the palate warms up again, the reduced blood flow means relief.

Serrador thinks a similar blood flow increase might be the root of migraines and other headaches. As for the torture that next milk shake could trigger? Drink more slowly. —*Catherine Zuckerman*

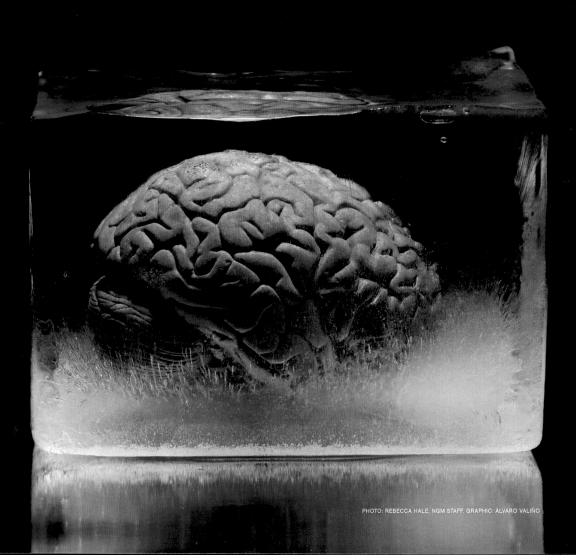

*After half a century
under Fidel, Cubans
feel a wary sense of
possibility. But this time,
don't expect a revolution.*

CUBA'S
NEW
NOW

A window reflects an image of Fidel Castro in a working-class Havana neighborhood few tourists see.

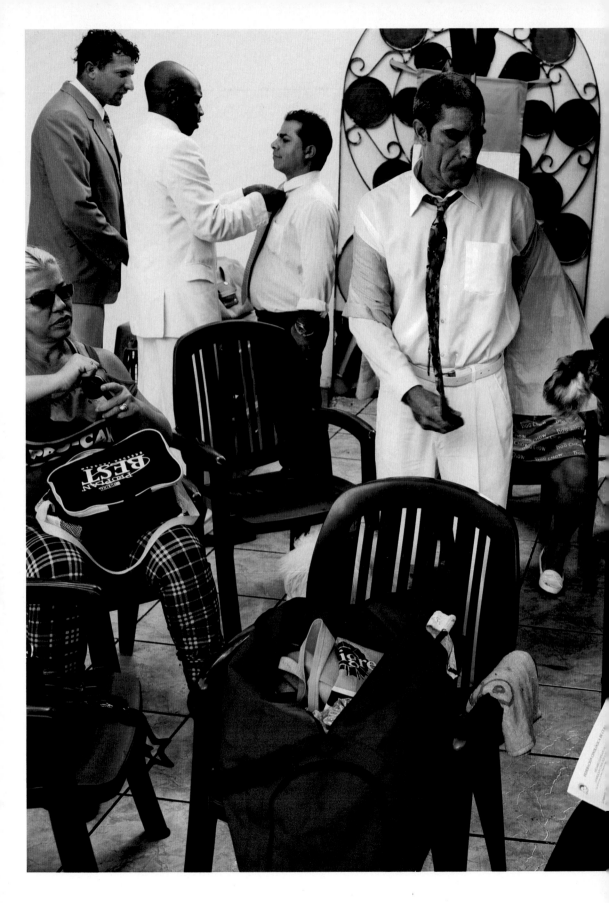

Dog owners prep at Havana's Champion of Champions show. Such flourishes of discretionary spending, a new option for Cubans with the right kind of currency, are a source of both pride and consternation.

The century-old stone wall of the Malecón, Havana's famous oceanside esplanade, shields the city—imperfectly—from the battering of roiling seas. On calmer nights people come out to stroll on the street.

Markers of a richly Cuban outing at Havana's Parque Lenin: the clicking of dominoes, the head-to-toe white clothing of a Santería adherent, and a Russian sedan likely kept running with transplanted parts.

By Cynthia Gorney
Photographs by Paolo Pellegrin

I "want to show you where we're hiding it," Eduardo said.

Bad idea, I said. Someone will notice the foreigner and wreck the plan.

"No, I figured it out," Eduardo said. "You won't get out of the car. I'll drive by, slowly, not so slow that we attract attention. I'll tell you when to look. Be discreet."

He had borrowed a friend's *máquina,* which means "machine" but is also what Cubans call the old American cars that are ubiquitous in the Havana souvenir postcards. This one was a 1956 Plymouth of a lurid color that I teased him about, but I pulled the passenger door shut gently, the way Cubans always remind you to, out of respect for their máquinas' advanced age. Now we were driving along the coast, some distance from Havana, into the coastal town where Eduardo and nine other men had paid a guy, in secret, to build a boat sturdy enough to motor them all out of Cuba at once.

"There," Eduardo said, and slowed the Plymouth. Between two peeling-paint buildings, on the inland side of the street, a narrow alley ended in a windowless structure the size of a one-car garage. "We'll have to carry it out and wheel it up the alley," he said. "Then it's a whole block along this main street, toward that gravel that leads into the water. We'll wait until after midnight. But navy helicopters patrol offshore."

He peered into his rearview mirror at the empty street behind him, concentrating, so I shut up. Eduardo is 35, a light-skinned Cuban with short brown hair and a wrestler's build, and in the months since we first met last winter—he's a former construction worker but that day was driving a borrowed Korean sedan and trying to earn money as an off-the-books cabdriver—we had taken to yelling good-naturedly and interrupting each other as we drove around La Habana Province, arguing about the New Changing Cuba. He said there was no such thing. I said people insisted there was. I invoked the many reports I was reading, with names like "Change in Post-Fidel Cuba" and "Cuba's New Resolve." Eduardo would gaze heavenward in exasperation. I invoked the much vaunted new rules opening up the controlled economy of socialist Cuba—the laws allowing people to buy and sell houses and cars openly, obtain bank loans, and work legally for themselves in a variety of small businesses rather than being obliged to work for the state.

But no. More eye rolling. "All that is for the benefit of these guys," Eduardo said to me once, and tapped his own shoulder, the discreet Cuban signal for a person with military hardware and inner-circle political pull.

What about Fidel Castro having permanently left the presidency four years ago, formally yielding the office of commander in chief to his more flexible and pragmatic younger brother, Raúl?

"*Viva Cuba Libre,*" Eduardo muttered, mimicking a revolutionary exhortation we'd seen emblazoned high on an outdoor wall. Long live free Cuba. "Free from both of them," he said. "That's when there might be real change."

If there is in fact a Cuba under serious transformation—and you can find Cubans all over the country engaging now in their own versions

A passenger rides shotgun in a Havana taxi—not the kind used by tourists, but one of the geriatric American cars that carry only Cubans, who pay a fraction of the tourist fare.

of this same debate—Eduardo is a crucial component of it, although not for the reasons you might think. "Dissident" is the right label for a subset of politically vocal Cubans, notably the bloggers whose critical online missives have gained big followings outside the country, but Eduardo is no sort of dissident. He's not fleeing persecution by the state. He's just young, energetic, and frustrated, a description that applies to a great many of his countrymen. Ever since he was a teenager in high school, Eduardo told me, it had been evident to him that adulthood in revolutionary Cuba offered exactly nothing by way of personal advancement and material comfort to anybody except the *peces gordos.* The big fish. (Well, literally translated, the fat fish—the tap-on-the-shoulder parties.) Nothing *works* here, Eduardo would cry, pounding the steering wheel of whatever car he'd hustled on loan for the day: The economic model is broken, state employees survive on their tiny salaries only by stealing from the jobsite, the national news outlets are an embarrassment of self-censored boosterism, the government makes people crazy by circulating two national currencies at once.

"I love my country," Eduardo kept saying. "But there is no future for me here."

Over nine weeks of traveling around Cuba this year and last, I heard this particular sequence of complaints so often, and from so many different kinds of people, that it began to form a kind of collective national lamentation: I love my country and it doesn't work. There were loyal optimists among the complainers, to be sure, and after a while, whenever I encountered one, I found myself marshaling ammunition to bring Eduardo. I wanted to hear how he'd respond, but when I was being honest with myself, I realized that I also wanted to talk him out of the boat. (Sharks swim in those Cuba-to-Florida waters. The currents are dangerous. There are drownings, people never heard from again.)

Optimist: Roberto Pérez, a shaggy-haired environmental biologist, filled with enthusiasm about the progress of Cuba's extensive urban

Cynthia Gorney is a contributing writer for the magazine who frequently reports from Latin America. Paolo Pellegrin is a Magnum photographer who lives in Rome and New York City.

agriculture and organic farming projects. Pérez is six years older than Eduardo. Eighty percent of his own high school graduating class, Pérez told me, has left the country. "But things *are* changing," he said. "Very fast. And there are so many good things here that people take for granted, because they were born with them. You tell me another place where a kid can grow up so safe, get his vaccinations, get his education, not be involved in gangs or drugs. I can see people crossing the river north from Mexico, to get away from that. But from here? To face the Florida strait? I fail to see it."

Still no? OK. Optimist: Josué López, exactly Eduardo's age, just immigrated back to Cuba after six years in Florida and a growing disenchantment with the values of some of his hyper-acquisitive Cuban émigré neighbors in Miami. López and his wife are going into business for themselves, taking advantage of the new self-employment laws and new flexibility in agricultural land use, and developing a bed-and-breakfast resort on a few acres they've acquired outside Havana. "I'm telling my friends who went to the States," López told me, in his practiced slangy English, "Dude! If you want to start something, the place to be is Cuba."

Eduardo would listen, interested, his face sober. He would shake his head. We were arguing in a café one morning, a rooftop spot in the historic part of Havana, and Eduardo grabbed a glass saltshaker from the table. "My whole *life,* the government has been telling us, Look! I'm giving you this nice full saltshaker!" he said. "But it's never full."

This one wasn't either. A half inch of salt, maybe. Eduardo put the shaker down and told me he had gotten hold of some oars. The men would have to row for a while, before they could risk motor noise that might alert authorities; the departure itself would violate Cuban law, since none of them had a *tarjeta blanca,* a white card, the government permission required of all citizens before they may leave the country, even temporarily. Cubans hate the tarjeta blanca, and the government subsequently hinted at doing away with it entirely—but on this early spring morning Eduardo hadn't even applied for one,

since he assumed the tarjeta would be denied, as they sometimes are, with no explanation beyond the bland, omnipresent *No está autorizado*—It is not authorized. Besides, a Cuban applying for a tarjeta blanca is supposed to have a visa from the destination country. Just to secure a spot on the consideration list for a U.S. visa, a Cuban must pay $160 and produce a written invitation from some actual person living in the United States.

Eduardo had neither. I had expected him to solicit help from me, the money or the invite, but he never did; he just blurted out the boat plan one day in the middle of a long, talky car ride, as though he'd been desperate for a non-Cuban confessor, and now here we were staring at a saltshaker and brooding about Eduardo's son, who was nine and didn't know his father was going.

"I don't know if it will be better to tell him or worse," he said.

At least the money he'd send home would buy his son new shoes, Eduardo said. "Everything has a risk in life," he said. "I'm not worried. Use my real name. I've told you this before. Use it! I'm not afraid of anybody!" He spread his arms wide, trying to look unworried, and repeated his name the Latin American way: first name, paternal surname, maternal surname. I told him to quit being foolish, that he still lived in a one-party state in which people get roughed up or arrested or excoriated as mercenaries for criticizing their leaders too vigorously, and that we were talking about this in public only because the café waiter was a friend of his and nobody else was nearby. So forget it, I said. Sorry. No real name. We were quiet. Beneath us spread the most famous district in Cuba, the streets the tourists want to see first. There were shining 19th-century tile work, the filigreed top of a Corinthian column, a glimpse of the turquoise sea.

THE WHOLE CITY seemed to be shining, that morning with Eduardo, even though there'd been a *derrumbe* in the neighborhood where I was staying. That's a building collapse, a thing that occurs with some regularity, especially in Havana. Buildings that were once beautiful and

grand are rotting now in the tropical air, and the country has no money to repair them, so they cave in, partially or all at once, a giant rumbling roar followed by rubble and grief. This der- rumbe killed four people, three of them teenage girls; the building had been designated unsafe, but Cubans are inventive about their living space in Havana, where parts of the city are so crowded that multiple families and generations wedge into residences that in more decadent eras served as single-family homes. Eduardo had the idea that the number of deaths in my neighborhood derrumbe was 21—he had heard this via *radio bemba,* the radio of lips, which is

to exchange residences but not to sell them, now appeared in house windows. In a few weeks Pope Benedict XVI was due to arrive, the first papal visit to Cuba in 14 years. Along the route the papal cortege would follow, state workers were cleaning and painting house facades so assidu- ously that I heard people joke that they wished the Holy Father would show up more often, just for the urban cleanup.

Hefty half-built structures stuck out here and there—the anti-derrumbes, as I came to think of them, into which the country's sparse invest- ment resources were being directed. High cranes and scaffolding delineated the rehabilitation of

HALF THE BUILDINGS' DOORWAYS SEEMED TO HAVE BEEN TAKEN OVER BY NEW SELF-EMPLOYED VENDORS, THE MEN AND WOMEN SITTING HOPEFULLY ALONGSIDE MAKESHIFT DISPLAYS.

what Cubans call the word on the street, the only censor-free method for the dissemination of discouraging domestic news. But I had been reading *Granma,* the national Communist Party daily, which to the surprise of many people had actually run articles about this derrumbe rather than pretending it had never occurred and was steadfast about the death toll of four. Anyway, the city looked shiny. The tourists were charging all over by the busload, maps in hand, and from what I could see they appeared to be having a great time, sipping their rum-and-mint *mojitos,* following their multilingual Cuban guides, and applauding the happy cacophony of rumba and *son* that spilled out into the plazas from restau- rants and street corners and bars.

Unmistakably, and provocatively, unusual things were transpiring in the streets. In some neighborhoods half the buildings' doorways seemed to have been taken over by new self- employed vendors, the men and women sitting hopefully alongside makeshift displays of hair accessories or homemade pastries or DVDs of movies and television shows. "For Sale" signs, prohibited during the decades when it was legal

historic buildings, the gussying up of tourist destinations, the construction of new port facili- ties. From certain spots along the shoreline, you could make out the shape of the huge deepwater rig exploring the Cuban seabed, believed to con- tain billions of barrels' worth of oil. If large-scale oil production is merited, the possibilities for the country's economic future are profound.

Most of the Cubans I talked to seemed con- sumed, in fact, by this whole idea of possibility. Not permanent transformation, most would say, not yet; the Cuban government has a history of switching signals on its citizens, encouraging pri- vate enterprise and then pronouncing it coun- terrevolutionary and shutting it down again. But Raúl Castro is not his brother, and there's a par- ticularly Cuban combination of excitement, wari- ness, calculation, black humor, and anxiety that accompanies even the possibility of real change— the suggestion that after a half century under Fi- del, something big may truly be happening to the way Cubans live day to day. "The rebuilding of the house of Cuba," an ecclesiastical lawyer and editor named Roberto Veiga said gravely, pronouncing the Spanish words with *(Continued on page 48)*

(Continued on page 48)

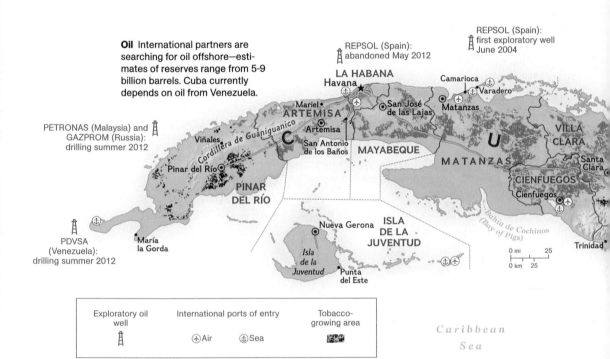

FLORIDA
(UNITED STATES)
Miami

Gulf of Mexico

Proximity to U.S. Tens of thousands of people have risked the 90-mile journey to South Florida.

Key West

Florida Keys

Straits *of* *Florida*

REPSOL (Spain): first exploratory well June 2004

Oil International partners are searching for oil offshore—estimates of reserves range from 5-9 billion barrels. Cuba currently depends on oil from Venezuela.

REPSOL (Spain): abandoned May 2012

LA HABANA
Havana

Camarioca
Varadero

PETRONAS (Malaysia) and GAZPROM (Russia): drilling summer 2012

Mariel
ARTEMISA
San José de las Lajas
Matanzas

Viñales
Cordillera de Guaniguanico
Artemisa
San Antonio de los Baños
MAYABEQUE

VILLA CLARA

Pinar del Río

MATANZAS

Santa Clara

PINAR DEL RÍO

CIENFUEGOS
Cienfuegos

PDVSA (Venezuela): drilling summer 2012

María la Gorda

Nueva Gerona
ISLA DE LA JUVENTUD

Bahía de Cochinos (Bay of Pigs)

Trinidad

Isla de la Juventud
Punta del Este

0 mi   25
0 km   25

Exploratory oil well

International ports of entry
⊕ Air   ⚓ Sea

Tobacco-growing area

Caribbean Sea

CUBANS OUT, DOLLARS IN

Among the most reliable sources of hard currency are the billions in remittances flowing in from the Cuban diaspora and the more than two billion dollars spent annually by tourists. The number of people leaving the island each year fluctuates with the twists and turns of politics and policy.

 Cuban native and NGS cartographer Juan Valdés narrates an emigration time line.

Postrevolutionary emigration and remittances

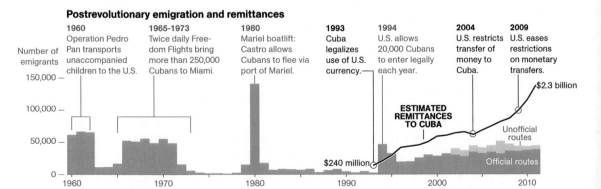

Number of emigrants

1960
Operation Pedro Pan transports unaccompanied children to the U.S.

1965-1973
Twice daily Freedom Flights bring more than 250,000 Cubans to Miami.

1980
Mariel boatlift: Castro allows Cubans to flee via port of Mariel.

1993
Cuba legalizes use of U.S. currency.

1994
U.S. allows 20,000 Cubans to enter legally each year.

2004
U.S. restricts transfer of money to Cuba.

2009
U.S. eases restrictions on monetary transfers.

150,000

$2.3 billion

100,000

ESTIMATED REMITTANCES TO CUBA

50,000

Unofficial routes

$240 million

Official routes

0

1960   1970   1980   1990   2000   2010

CAN CUBA STAY AFLOAT?

Hampered by the U.S. embargo and the collapse of the U.S.S.R. in 1991, Cuba's economy has floundered. Today it is precariously propped up by Venezuelan aid. Production of sugar—and most agricultural and industrial products—has plummeted since the 1959 revolution. Its best hope for growth: oil, nickel—and people. Tourism is up, along with cash sent to residents from abroad.

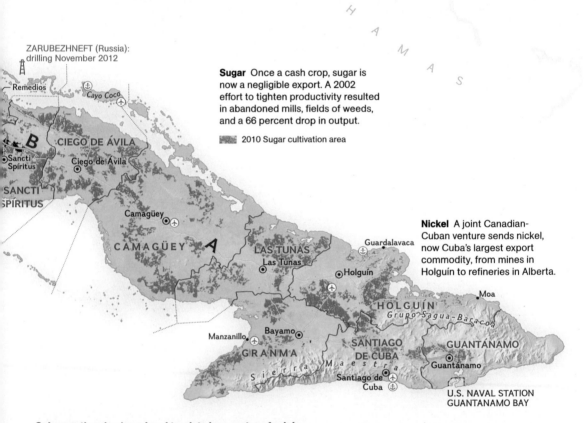

ZARUBEZHNEFT (Russia): drilling November 2012

Sugar Once a cash crop, sugar is now a negligible export. A 2002 effort to tighten productivity resulted in abandoned mills, fields of weeds, and a 66 percent drop in output.

2010 Sugar cultivation area

Nickel A joint Canadian-Cuban venture sends nickel, now Cuba's largest export commodity, from mines in Holguín to refineries in Alberta.

U.S. NAVAL STATION
GUANTANAMO BAY

Cuban nationals abroad and tourists by country of origin

■ = 5,000 emigrants (total for most recent data available, 2007-2011)   ■ = 5,000 tourists (2011 figures)

	United States	Spain	Germany	Pakistan	Mexico	Venezuela	Italy	Canada	Kuwait	Haiti
emigrants	1,104,679 68% in Florida	92,583	18,265	13,050	12,108	9,621	9,569	8,865	6,258	4,951
tourists	605,354 85% Cuban Americans	101,631	95,124		76,326	34,096	110,432	1,002,318		

MARTIN GAMACHE, NGM STAFF; ALEXANDER STEGMAIER AND JUAN JOSÉ VALDÉS, NG MAPS

SOURCES: CUBAN NATIONAL STATISTICS OFFICE; FAO; U.S. CENSUS; U.S. CUSTOMS AND BORDER PROTECTION; UN STATISTICS DIVISION; DEVELOPMENT RESEARCH CENTRE ON MIGRATION, GLOBALISATION AND POVERTY; MIGRATION POLICY INSTITUTE; EMILIO MORALES AND JOE SCARPACI, HAVANA CONSULTING GROUP; ARCH RITTER, CARLETON UNIVERSITY; JORGE R. PIÑON, UNIVERSITY OF TEXAS AT AUSTIN; MODIS LAND COVER, NASA LP DAAC

Movies, music, and TV shows are popular merchandise for Cuba's burgeoning private entrepreneurs. Discreet customer queries can sometimes unearth DVDs too racy—or politically inflammatory—for display.

For the first time in decades Cubans are allowed to buy and sell houses and apartments. Makeshift ads, fluttering from tree trunks, have turned Havana's Parque del Prado into an open-air real estate bazaar.

Hunting down groceries in poorly stocked markets, like this butcher shop in central Havana, is a daily challenge. Cubans receive ration books that secure staples like rice, beans, and oil at low prices. But it's not enough to live on.

Shoppers wait in line at a central Havana market. Poor management and decades of a U.S. embargo have crippled Cuba's agriculture. The country imports most of its food.

(Continued from page 39) the elegance of a pastor at the pulpit: *La reconstrucción de la casa Cuba*.

Careful, though: The rebuilding metaphor implies a blueprint. Those outside Cuba who imagine that this blueprint is agreed to by some clear Cuban consensus are deluding themselves. The unconstrained individualism of the United States, where neither health care nor a college education are free? The showy wealth and environmental havoc of modern China? The economic woes and internal tensions of Europe? The narco wars of Mexico? "This is our great challenge," Veiga told me. He helps run a publication of the Archdiocese of Havana, *Espacio Laical* (literally, *Secular Space*), which, like the Cuban Roman Catholic Church itself, has become one of the few venues in which semicritical debate about the country's future is aired in public. "What will it be like, this house of Cuba?" Veiga asked. "These are changes that should have begun two decades ago. But they didn't. And now we are a nation trying to define itself."

Eleven million people live in Cuba, less than the population of central Tokyo. It's the biggest island in the Caribbean, and famously only 90 miles from United States territory, but Cuba still grips the international imagination mostly because the dueling narratives of its history are so exaggerated by myth. Either a ruthless revolutionary took power in 1959, seized American corporate property, forced out his country's own professional classes, and silenced all opposition by creating a totalitarian police state (that's the version audible to this day on Miami's Radio Mambí, the broadcast voice of Florida's most vehement anti-Castro community); or a brilliant revolutionary led the overthrow of a corrupt dictatorship, shook off the colonialism of foreign companies and the Mafia, brought literacy and health care and egalitarian values to a mobilized people, and created a university-educated bastion of socialism in spite of a half century of U.S. efforts to destroy it by prohibiting Americans from doing business with or spending tourist money in Cuba.

Both narratives contain substantial truth, both at the same time. This is why Cuba fascinates and makes people's heads hurt. The place is exhausting in its complexity and paradoxes—Cubans are the first to tell you that—and the questions modern Cuba sets off in a visitor

In a government office in Viñales a receptionist labors under a portrait of retired leader Fidel Castro and a sign proclaiming that work must be orderly, disciplined, and demanding.

are big, serious, unwieldy. What is the definition of freedom? What do human beings need? What do they owe to each other? What do they want, beyond what they need? "We've all been the subjects of an experiment," a 58-year-old university-educated woman who works in the arts told me thoughtfully one evening, chopping sweet peppers in her kitchen for supper. She lives in an airy place, with a fenced front lawn and a backyard patio, in a leafy part of Havana; the home has belonged to her family since before the Triunfo, the Triumph of the Revolution, as Cubans generally refer to the events of 1959. Her lightbulbs are compact fluorescents, the woman pointed out—one legacy of an ambitious national project a few years back, directing all Cubans to switch to lower watt fixtures in the interests of energy independence and the environment.

"They'd come to check," she said. "They would break your old bulbs, in front of you, to make sure you didn't sneak any back into your lamps." She smiled and looked over her glasses at me to make sure I was listening closely enough. She has one child, a son a decade younger than Eduardo—gone now, having bailed out on Cuba

and obtained a therapy credential in Spain. "The idea was marvelous, to change all the lightbulbs," she said. "The problem is how they did it."

IN ITS HEADLINE VERSION, the rebuilding of the house of Cuba looks like this: Capitalism intrudes, around the edges, small bits at a time. Since 2010 more than 150,000 Cuban workers have left or been laid off from their state jobs, a concept previously unimaginable in a system that was supposed to provide all the work and all the social benefits. President Castro himself has said that the state apparatus is bloated and too conducive to dependence and corruption, and that the state must trim a half million workers. State agricultural land is now being leased in pieces to private farmers and cooperatives, and other kinds of legal self-employment are being gingerly promoted as well. Over the past two years the government has authorized 181 job-specific categories of *cuentapropismo,* as it's called—the keeping of one's own account.

Even the ration book—the *libreta* issued to all Cuban households, with its check-off columns for the state-subsidized basic foods every citizen

is supposed to get each month—may be an artifact near the end of its time, Raúl Castro has said. The libreta! This is big. Nothing is more evocative of the bewildering Cuban economy, and Cubans' complicated reaction to it, than the baseball card-size libreta, each one stapled together from thin cardboard and white paper and listing the items the holder may buy at artificially low prices: rice, sugar, and milk, if the family includes children under eight. There are squares to be checked off by hand. The pages look like the accounting ledgers of Dickensian clerks.

Here are things I have watched Cubans do with the libreta:

Reinforce its fraying cover carefully with decorative paper and tape.

Hold it in one hand, a plastic shopping bag in the other, while sweating in the moist heat, gossiping with neighbors, waiting for subsidized bread.

Whip it from their purses or off kitchen shelves, shoving the opened pages at me, exclaiming simultaneously that it demonstrates Cubans' care for each other and that the allotments have been so cut back the government might as well be trying to starve them all.

Once I was in the home of a priest of Santería, the Afro-Cuban religious practice that is the faith even of many professed Cuban Catholics. I was still trying to compose myself because the priest had just completed an initiation ceremony that included slitting the necks of pigeons and chickens and bleeding their corpses into sacred dishes and praying in Yoruba. But what the priest really wanted to talk about was his libreta. "Look at this!" he cried. "Eight ounces of oil, per person, for a month! Ten ounces of beans! One package of pasta maybe every three months!"

There's a term Cuban housewives use as they make their rounds in search of the day's family food: *pollo por pescado*. It means "chicken for fish": You have promised fish for dinner, but in the stores there is no fish, so you get a little chicken and pretend it's your fish. Cuba is surrounded by seawater, of course. Where is all the fish? Ah, any Cuban will tell you, leaning in close, a merry gleam in his eye: glad you asked, *mi amor*. The fish is in the restaurants. The fish is in the hotel buffets, a popular amenity for tourists, where long counters are piled high with varieties and quantities of food no ordinary Cuban ever sees. The fish is being sold out of private homes, if you know which doorbell to ring.

In many of these locales the fish—like nearly every desirable product in Cuba, from nightclub admission to hair dye and plasma TVs and acid-washed blue jeans—is being sold in CUCs.

Now we come to that aspect of present-day Cuba that causes the *yuma* (that's the grammatically adaptable slang for "American," "foreigner," and also "the general outside world to the north and east") to reach for a calculator and some aspirin and a crash course in recent Cuban history. The CUC, which is shorthand for Cuban convertible peso, is one of the two official currencies of Cuba. Like the libreta, the double-currency system is in theory destined for extinction; things are so fluid in Cuba that by the time you read this, it's conceivable the government will have begun ending it. But to appreciate fully the elaborate survival negotiations that have dominated so many Cubans' daily lives in recent years, you have to come to grips with the essential weirdness of the CUC.

It's a recently invented currency, introduced a decade ago as a replacement for the dollars and other foreign money that began flooding and disrupting the country after the Soviet Union collapsed in 1991, thus ending the big-socialists-to-little-socialists financial support that had been holding up the Cuban economy. The multiyear Cuban depression that followed the Soviet breakup was catastrophic (fuel shortages, 14-hour blackouts, widespread hunger), and the government set out to counter it by throwing the island open to international tourism. This was all done rather fiercely, with a flurry of beach hotel building that continues to this day—current plans include multiple golf courses and jet-capacity airports—while anti-capitalist admonishments still declaim from highway billboards and urban walls:

SOCIALISM OR DEATH!

THE CHANGES MEAN *MORE* SOCIALISM!

In its purest concept the CUC is used for goods and services somehow connected to foreignness: hotel bills, international transactions, Fidel T-shirts in the souvenir shops, and so on. One CUC is worth about one U.S. dollar, and it's simple to obtain them; whether you're a yuma or a Cuban, state employees at exchange centers will take whatever currency you hand them and count out your reciprocal CUCs, wishing you a pleasant day when they're done.

These employees, like the rest of the Cubans who work for the state—currently about 80 percent of the country's labor force—are not paid in CUCs. They're paid in the other currency, the

other basic foods not on the family libreta can be purchased in pesos, as can Cuban books, baseball game tickets, fares on the crowded public buses, and admission to museums and movie theaters and the ballet. The currency in which he is paid as a doctor will buy Dr. M the very kind of 1960s ascetic nationalism Che Guevara liked to espouse—in other words, as long as Señora M uses only the poor-quality peso soap, the M family brews only the peso coffee that comes with fillers ground in, and nobody ever buys deodorant.

"The toy truck I wanted for my son, with the little motor and remote control?" Dr. M said,

ABOUT 80 PERCENT OF CUBA'S LABOR FORCE WORKS FOR THE STATE. THE WORKPLACE PHILOSOPHY THIS INSPIRES: "THEY PRETEND TO PAY US, WHILE WE PRETEND TO WORK."

Cuban national peso. One national peso is worth 1/24 of a CUC, or just over four cents, and in socialist Cuba state salaries are fixed; the range as of mid-2012 was between about 250 and 900 pesos a month. Some workers now receive a CUC stimulus to augment their peso wages, and recent changes are lifting top-end salary limits and linking pay more to productivity than to preset increments. But it was Cubans who taught me the national comic line about public workplace philosophy: "They pretend to pay us, while we pretend to work."

IN THE CITY OF SANTA CLARA, where the principal attraction is a massive monument to revolutionary martyr Ernesto "Che" Guevara (fought with Fidel, died trying to foment insurrection in Bolivia), I spent an afternoon with a visiting emergency physician whose medical salary was fixed at 785.35 national pesos per month. That works out to CUC\$32.72. Like so much about Cuba, this isn't straightforward; Dr. M owes nothing for his professional education and his own family's medical care. His son's lifetime schooling is free. Produce and certain

as we stood side by side beneath the gigantic monument pedestal, craning our necks up at Che. "Forty CUCs."

Forty CUCs in a state store, that is. Cubans maintain a robust black market—*por la izquierda,* they call it, "over to the left"—in which anything can be obtained. But the most surrealistic aspect of life in Cuba 2012 is the vigor with which the government, the same entity paying Cubans in pesos, sells goods to Cubans in CUCs. Retail stores, like pharmaceutical factories and nickel mines, are national enterprises, run by the state. Clerks often don't bother specifying "CUC" on the pricing of merchandise either; if a thing whirs or glitters or comes in good packaging, Cubans know the currency in which it is being sold, and regardless of whatever the ghost of Che may be whispering in their ear, they want it.

By the time I met Dr. M, I had done so much confounded window-shopping that there were numbers all over my notebooks: Pepsodent toothpaste, CUC\$1.50 per tube. Electric blender, CUC\$113.60. Upholstered loveseat-and-armchair living room set, CUC\$597.35.

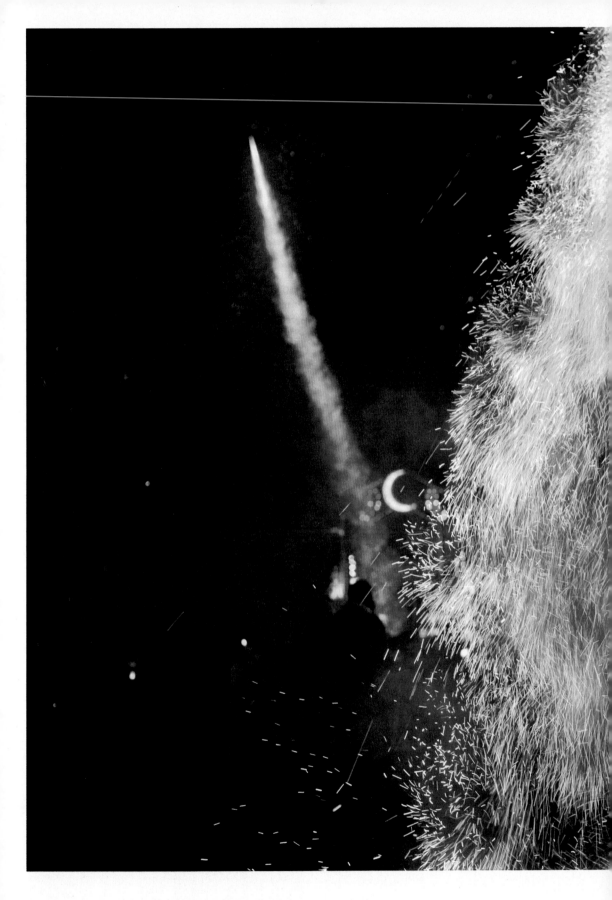

A plume of fireworks surrounds a reveler at the Parrandas, a December festival in the colonial town of Remedios, near Cuba's north coast. Two barrios compete to stage the most impressive display.

Until the 1959 ouster of dictator Fulgencio Batista, Cuba's legislature convened in the domed Capitolio building in Havana. Today it's a symbol of a prerevolutionary Cuba that no one under the age of 50 experienced.

Multistory malls, with cafés and video game halls and clothing stores, all functioning exclusively in CUCs.

The cell phones Cubans depend upon—pre-Raúl they were prohibited; now they're everywhere—are sold, both the device and the per-minute fees, in CUCs. Even a Bucanero Fuerte, one of the good Cuban beers, is likely to be sold in CUCs. The Bucanero price of one CUC, not an unreasonable sum in many countries for a bottle of beer, constitutes a full day's medical pay for Dr. M. You see the problem with the toy truck. This is why for four days a week, when he's supposed to be recuperating from his 24-hour emergency shifts, Dr. M drives a cab.

Technically, he drives his own car, the aged Russian beater he inherited from his father. But he picks up tourists in it, because tourists pay in CUCs. Over one high-season month Dr. M's cabbie days earn him the CUC equivalent of 15 times his salary as a physician. In Cuba there's nothing remarkable about this. The taxi fleet, like the rest of the tourist industry, is replete with splendidly educated Cubans no longer practicing their professions because their years of study to be of service to the nation—in engineering, medicine, psychology—produced salaries in "the money that's worthless," as a kindly Cuban bank teller once remarked to me. The phenomenon is referred to as the "inverted pyramid." Every Cuban who repeated that term to me did so in a tone of despair, as in: This, you see, is why the ambitious young keep leaving.

Dr. M and I studied the object Che was holding in his giant fist above us, determined that it was a hand grenade, and went into the museum. Che Guevara was an Argentine medical school graduate when he met Fidel Castro, and as we walked past the glass-encased displays of the Che medical journals and the Che lab coat, I glanced over at Dr. M. In the 15 years since Che's ashes were delivered to Santa Clara, Dr. M told me, this was the first time he had visited the museum. But he was silent and impassive, and when we came out, all he said was, "I don't get this about us now—how a taxi driver can make so much more than a doctor."

The expression on his face made it clear that Che Guevara was not a topic he wished to continue exploring. "I don't get it," he said.

EDUARDO TOLD ME the boat's departure date was set, depending on what the men could learn about tide and weather predictions, for the days just after the pope's visit ended. When I was away from Havana, in the island's interior, text messages from his number showed up every so often on my temporary Cuban phone: "hi my friend am going soon on vacation."

I was doing a lot of walking, or strapping on flimsy passenger helmets and climbing (imprudently) onto the backs of unlicensed motorcycle taxis. To my outsider's eye, the New Changing Cuba looked both real and raggedy, as though an enormous flea market had been busted up and scattered the length of the country. Young men sat in stairwells, offering to repair cell phones or refill cigarette lighters. Families lined their front porches with display tables of used kitchen merchandise or thermoses of coffee and chipped plates of wrapped ham-and-cheese sandwiches.

Here were small corner businesses that used to be run by the state but now, experimentally, were not: barbershops and snack bars, for example, in which management was being transferred to the employees. Here was a former high school math teacher, a soft-spoken 42-year-old who had learned to speak Russian fluently back in the comfortable days of life support from the U.S.S.R. Now he was selling baby clothes for CUCs from one corner of a rented street-front foyer in the central city of Camagüey. "My wife does the sewing," the former math teacher said. "She used to be a teacher too."

And here, in the middle of one residential block back in Havana, was a chic new restaurant called Le Chansonnier. No signage marked the entrance; Le Chansonnier is a *paladar,* a privately run restaurant inside a home, and people with money—correction, people with CUCs—know where it is. Paladares have been legal for years in Cuba but used to be strictly contained, under the pretense that they were all tiny family operations siphoning no business from state

restaurants. Since 2011, though, they've been allowed to expand and hire staff, and like the guest rooms Cubans may rent to foreigners inside their own homes and apartments, some of the popular paladares have basically turned into busy CUC cash registers for their owners. "I always dreamed of having my own business," the co-owner, a 39-year-old named Héctor Higuera Martínez, told me the afternoon I stopped by. "I used to think I'd be an engineer. But I saw that there was a living in working with tourists."

Higuera waved a hand at somebody and in short order produced an amazing salad for me, with beautiful butter lettuce, shaved chicken, people who've left it. And because both the U.S. and Cuban governments have eased restrictions on émigrés returning to visit family, the Cuban Americans who arrive to weepy reunion embraces at the Havana airport are usually carrying both money and goods: televisions, appliances, duffel bags full of clothing, and anything else their relatives can resell por la izquierda for CUCs.

There's stealing too, which during the post-Soviet-collapse depression years emerged as a nationwide mechanism for family survival. The verb *luchar*, which means "fight," also translates loosely in Cuba to "transfer workplace items into one's personal possession, which the system

MANY CUBANS NO LONGER PRACTICE THEIR PROFESSIONS BECAUSE YEARS OF STUDY—IN ENGINEERING, MEDICINE—PRODUCED SALARIES IN A CURRENCY THAT'S WORTHLESS.

and a dusting of chocolate. He was trying to figure out how to manage the evening's multiple parties of ten; dinner at Le Chansonnier, which draws foreigners and Cubans alike, runs about 40 CUCs per person. His business partner, Laura Fernández Córdoba, who's run the restaurant with him since they opened in fall 2011 with the help of French investors, was approving a tableware purchase in the next room. It was easy to envision money flying in and out of the building, in a New Changing Cuba sort of way, and part of what had been flummoxing me during my early weeks in Cuba was starting to come clear. Not every Cuban drives a taxi or tends bar for tourist tips, right? So how on Earth, I had wondered every time I examined all the nonpeso merchandise being hawked at Cubans from every direction, were they accumulating these CUCs?

Part of the answer is remittances, the dollars and euros sent from relatives abroad. The amount of money sent to Cuba annually is hard to track, but some economists estimate the number may surpass $2 billion this year. That means the modern Cuban state is being nourished partly by impels us to do because our salaries won't cover a lousy Bucanero." The standard lucha involves eating, drinking, using, bartering, or selling the items in question. Reform campaigns pushed by Raúl Castro have produced scores of high-level corruption arrests, but one defining quality of any attractive workplace, still, is the nature of the lucha. ("If you can't look around and find things you can take home or resell," a woman in her 40s from a working-class neighborhood outside Havana told me firmly, "then it's not a good job.")

Nothing about this combination, remittances plus pilfering, is unusual in a small tropical country without abundant raw material for export. Neither is the third important way CUCs arrive in Cubans' pockets: legal commerce, of any sort, that directly or indirectly procures foreigners' money. But the government of the Cuban *proyecto socialista,* or socialist project—in official dispatches that remains the preferred term—has tried for a half century to wall off much of the country from the very buy-sell system that generated that money in the first place. Watching Cubans grapple, as they consider just how many of those walls ought now

to be dismantled, is a sobering experience. Take Higuera and Fernández: Their private, for-profit business and their ten employees are legal under the new self-employment laws, as long as they pay their taxes.

But business taxes, in themselves a relatively new concept in Cuba, increase sharply as employers hire more people. The system is weighted against much private expansion while Cubans experiment with new tax and regulation policies, and this question of limits—of just how successful individual entrepreneurs should aspire to become—is a matter of great philosophical and political contention in the New Changing

"We just don't know yet," a veteran University of Havana economist named Juan Triana Cordoví told me, when I asked about guideline number three. "You can do this big bang style, as Russia did, but I don't think that worked very well. Or you can do it step-by-step, watching what will happen. I am one of the ones who prefer step-by-step. I think of it as testing the stones of the river, one foot at a time, to see if each stone will hold."

I could see how the guidelines, which were released to great fanfare, might look from a certain perspective like one more saltshaker only a quarter full. This is why so many young people spend a lot of time talking to their peers

WHAT MIGHT THEY SAY, I WONDERED, IF THEY COULD TALK DIRECTLY TO A CUBAN I KNEW BUYING CANNED TUNA THIS VERY WEEK FOR AN ILLEGAL DEPARTURE INTO THE STRAITS OF FLORIDA?

Cuba. Last year, after months of discussions around the country, a remarkable official document called "Guidelines for the Economic and Social Policy of the Party and the Revolution" was published—313 guidelines, to be exact, each one addressing a specific subject, like land use or the civic importance of sports. Guideline number three declares that the "concentration of property" by individuals, as opposed to the state, "will not be permitted."

What does that mean, exactly? The guidelines don't say. The cynical will tell you it means the government shall countenance no threat, no real business competition, to the bureaucracies and personal fiefdoms of government companies. The less cynical will tell you that it means Cuba must manage this move toward privatization carefully, while trying to protect the services Cubans have come to expect—that there remains some genuine national conviction in Cuba, no matter how exhausted the SOCIALISM OR DEATH! slogans may now appear to the young, that it's deeply wrong for certain citizens of a nation to make themselves thousands of times wealthier than others.

about their futures in Cuba, about whether to stay or go. There are multiple routes away now, most much safer than little boats pushed out to sea in the dark. Family members wait out the long delays for visas to join relatives abroad. Professionals overseas on Cuban service missions, like the thousands of medical professionals and sports trainers now working in Venezuela, sometimes decline to return home. "You're always trying to convince people not to leave," Higuera said. "Always. I have a friend in Madrid now. He got there just in time for the crash."

What might he and Fernández say, I wondered, if they could talk directly to a Cuban I knew, halfway between their two ages, buying canned tuna this very week for an illegal departure into the Straits of Florida?

Higuera sighed. "I'd say to him, If you're going to do this thing, do it," he said.

I had heard this before, after asking other Cubans the same question, and it still surprised me a little; I expected to hear the word *gusano*, worm, which in an earlier era was the famous public castigation for anybody who abandoned

Cockfighting is a long-standing tradition that survived the revolution and thrives in rural settings. This young Cuban cradles a contestant in the province of Pinar del Río.

the revolution. But I never did. People would nod and say they understood. Or they'd point to a framed picture—on a wall, hanging from a rearview mirror—of a relative who'd already done the same thing. "But I'd tell him to make sure he's doing it for himself, not somebody else's expectation of him," Higuera said. "And I'd ask him to look hard at what he sees in other places. I really do have hope that things are improving here."

A week later I went home, and I waited for Eduardo to call me collect, as we'd both arranged, from somewhere in South Florida. Two weeks passed without a call. Then another week, and then another. I tried the Havana cell phone Eduardo had been using, but there was no answer, and finally I called his brother, who immigrated to Mexico a few years ago to marry a Mexican woman he had met in Cuba.

The phone connection was bad, and I wasn't sure how much was safe to say. I was an American who had befriended Eduardo in Havana, I said, and I just wondered—how he was, that was all. I said he had spoken of an impending vacation. His brother became very excited. "He didn't

make it," he said in Spanish. He was shouting into the phone. "There was a problem with the boat. *El timón.* They didn't make it."

I didn't have my dictionary in reach, and I didn't know what a timón was, and all I could think was that it was like *tiburón,* which means shark. *"Tell me what that means,"* I said urgently, and Eduardo's brother said he didn't know how to describe it exactly but that it was a boat part, a thing that had failed before they were too far out, and it was all right, they had used the oars, they were back in Cuba. No one was arrested. He was going to wait a while, Eduardo's brother said, and stay in their mother's apartment with his wife while he saved some more money.

After we hung up I got the dictionary. A timón is a rudder. I had a picture in my mind now, what had happened to Eduardo: Floating in the sea, the rudder broken, he and his companions had surely discussed it for a time, what would happen if they tried to motor on, toward a landfall they couldn't see, with nothing beneath them to keep the direction true. Then they turned the boat around, back into the piece of the ocean they already knew, and rowed home. ☐

ESCAPE

Preparing to launch from the sea to the sea ice, an emperor penguin reaches maximum speed.

VELOCITY

Awkward on land, emperor penguins soar through the sea.
Now scientists have discovered the secret of their speed.

An airborne penguin shows why it has
a need for speed: To get out of the water,
it may have to clear several feet of ice.
A fast exit also helps it elude leopard seals,
which often lurk at the ice edge.

ROGER HUGHES has never seen emperor penguins in the wild. But when he saw them in a BBC documentary, rocketing through the sea with trails of bubbles in their wakes, he had an insight that would lead to a surprising discovery. A marine biologist at Bangor University in north Wales, Hughes had recently been talking with his wife about the lubricating properties of new competitive swimsuits. He wondered: Maybe those bubbles help penguins swim faster.

Over beer in a pub, Hughes bounced his hypothesis off his friend John Davenport, a marine biologist at University College Cork in Ireland. "Roger thought I'd have the answer straightaway," says Davenport, who studies the relationship between animals' body structures and their movements. But he didn't know what the bubbles did for the penguins. It turns out no one else knew either. The two men combed the scientific literature and found that the phenomenon had never even been studied. So they decided to do it themselves.

With the help of Poul Larsen, a mechanical engineer at the Technical University of Denmark, they analyzed hours of underwater footage and discovered that the penguins were doing something that engineers had long tried to do with boats and torpedoes: They were using air as a lubricant to cut drag and increase speed.

When an emperor penguin swims through the water, it is slowed by the friction between its body and the water, keeping its maximum speed somewhere between four and nine feet a second. But in short bursts the penguin can double or even triple its speed by releasing air from its feathers in the form of tiny bubbles. These reduce the density and viscosity of the water around the penguin's body, cutting drag and enabling the bird to reach speeds that would otherwise be impossible. (As an added benefit, the extra speed helps the penguins avoid predators such as leopard seals.)

The key to this talent is in the penguin's feathers. Like other birds, emperors have the capacity to fluff their feathers and insulate their bodies with a layer of air. But whereas most birds have rows of feathers with bare skin between them, emperor penguins have a dense, uniform coat of feathers. And because the bases of their feathers include tiny filaments—just 20 microns in diameter, less than half the width of a thin human hair—air is trapped in a fine, downy mesh and released as microbubbles so tiny that they form a lubricating coat on the feather surface.

Though feathers are not an option for ships, technology may finally be catching up with biology. In 2010 a Dutch company started selling systems that lubricate the hulls of containerships with bubbles. Last year Mitsubishi announced that it had designed an air-lubrication system for supertankers. But so far no one has designed anything that can gun past a leopard seal and launch over a wall of sea ice. That's still proprietary technology. —*Glenn Hodges*

Seeing Penguins From Space
Recent analysis of satellite imagery identified four new colonies and nearly doubled the total estimated population of emperor penguins.

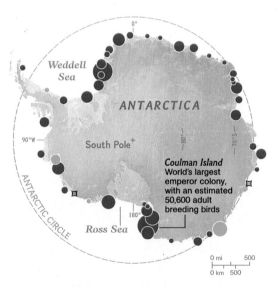

Weddell Sea

ANTARCTICA

90°W

South Pole

Coulman Island
World's largest emperor colony, with an estimated 50,600 adult breeding birds

ANTARCTIC CIRCLE

Ross Sea

0 mi 500
0 km 500

● **Emperor penguin colony**
(46 identified, as of 2009)

● Discovered in 2009

⌂ No current population estimate

Estimated colony population
(Global total: 595,000*)

50,000 adult breeding birds
20,000
<3,000

*Includes nonbreeding adults

MAGGIE SMITH, NGM STAFF. SOURCES: BRITISH ANTARCTIC SURVEY; POLAR GEOSPATIAL CENTER, UNIVERSITY OF MINNESOTA

PENGUINS HIT THE GAS

Emperor penguins are famous for their spectacular leaps
from the water, but only recently have scientists begun to
understand the blend of body mechanics and physics
that helps these flightless birds soar.

Penguin
feather

Ice layer

Sometimes
penguins follow
the air path
of others.

Leopard
seal threat

Speed
6.5
feet/second

Speed
18
feet/second

45 feet

1. Fueling up

After foraging, penguins may preen at the
surface, filling their plumage with air. Then
they'll dive, make sure the coast is clear, and
start building speed for an explosive exit.

2. Pouring on the power

For a final surge of speed, air is released
from the feathers, coating an emperor's
body with a thin layer of tiny bubbles
that reduces drag caused by friction.

Detail below

Airflow

Microbubbles

Water

Outer portion

Inner portion

Barb

Air layer

Barbules

Nodes

Downy feathers at
the base of each
shaft are made up of
microscopic filaments
that help hold a layer
of air near the body.

Elastic
membrane

Muscles attached to a
flexible membrane enable
penguins to change the
position of their feathers,
allowing air in or out.

ART: FERNANDO G. BAPTISTA, NGM STAFF; TONY SCHICK. PHOTO: REBECCA HALE, NGM STAFF (FEATHER)
SOURCES: JOHN DAVENPORT, UNIVERSITY COLLEGE CORK, IRELAND; JULIE C. HAGELIN, UNIVERSITY OF
ALASKA FAIRBANKS; SMITHSONIAN INSTITUTION, DIVISION OF BIRDS (FEATHER)

iPad/Kindle Fire
Learn more about
how emperor
penguins swim.

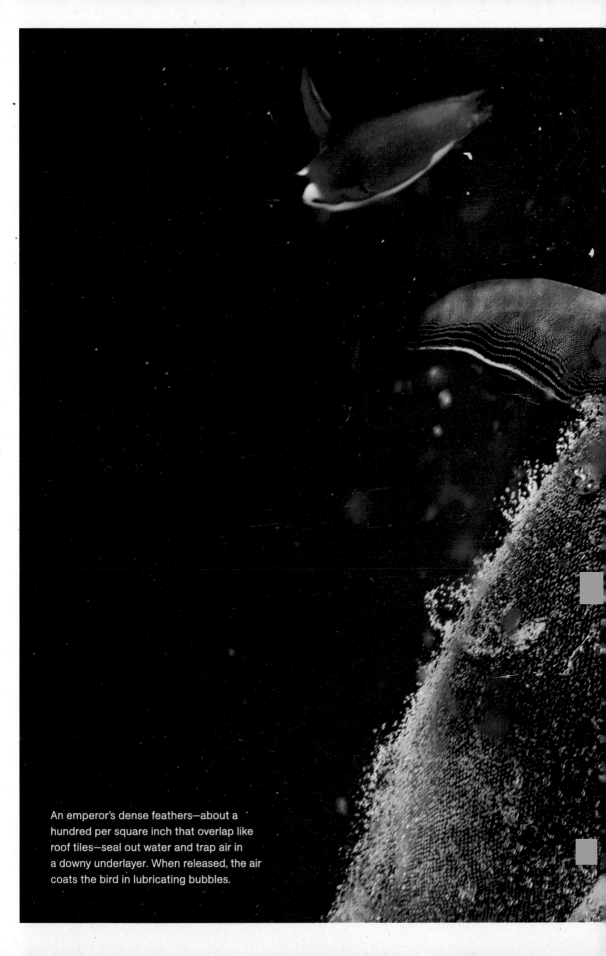

An emperor's dense feathers—about a
hundred per square inch that overlap like
roof tiles—seal out water and trap air in
a downy underlayer. When released, the air
coats the bird in lubricating bubbles.

After hunting at sea to get food for their chicks, adult penguins swim at the surface, which loads their plumage with air. Then they'll dive deep, gather speed, and race toward their exit hole.

At a colony on the frozen Ross Sea, emperor parents and chicks bask in the brief summer sun. The distance to open water varies with the season; in midwinter birds may have to cross many miles of ice to feed.

The danger of ambush by leopard seals
is greatest when entering the water,
so penguins sometimes linger at the edge
of an ice hole for hours, waiting for one
bold bird to plunge in. Life is safer at the
colony (left), where predators are few
and company is close.

Emperors can bolt away for any number of reasons, as photographer Paul Nicklen discovered when he spooked this group. "A tenth of a second after I took this picture, all I could see were bubbles."

Without the safety of numbers, a lone penguin
corkscrews to get a 360-degree view of its
surroundings. When it leaps from the water,
it will land with a thump and a squeak and
leave its most graceful moves behind.

VIKINGS
and NATIVE
AMERICANS

face-to-face

Following a subtle trail of artifacts,
a Canadian archaeologist searches for
a lost chapter of New World history.

BY HEATHER PRINGLE

PHOTOGRAPHS BY DAVID COVENTRY

New clues suggest that the ancient Americans who carved this fierce mask may have dealt with Viking explorers on friendly terms.

Daring Viking seafarers used ships like this modern replica to reach the New World in their search for furs, walrus ivory, and trading partners—which they may have found in the native Dorset people.

VIKING SHIP MUSEUM, ROSKILDE, DENMARK

SOMETHING ABOUT
THE STRANGE STRANDS
DIDN'T FIT.

Patricia Sutherland spotted it right away: the weird fuzziness of them, so soft to the touch.

The strands of cordage came from an abandoned settlement at the northern tip of Canada's Baffin Island, far above the Arctic Circle and north of Hudson Bay. There indigenous hunters had warmed themselves by seal-oil lamps some 700 years ago. In the 1980s a Roman Catholic missionary had also puzzled over the soft strands after digging hundreds of delicate objects from the same ruins. Made of short hairs plucked from the pelt of an arctic hare, the cordage bore little resemblance to the sinew that Arctic hunters twisted into string. How did it come to be here? The answer eluded the old priest, so he boxed up the strands with the rest of his finds

and delivered them to the Canadian Museum of Civilization in Gatineau, Quebec.

Years passed. Then one day in 1999 Sutherland, an Arctic archaeologist at the museum, slipped the strands under a microscope and saw that someone had spun the short hairs into soft yarn. The prehistoric people of Baffin Island, however, were neither spinners nor weavers; they stitched their clothing from skins and furs. So where could this spun yarn have come from? Sutherland had an inkling. Years earlier, while helping to excavate a Viking farmhouse in Greenland, she had seen colleagues dig bits of similar yarn from the floor of a weaving room. She promptly got on the phone to an archaeologist in Denmark. Weeks later an expert on

Donny Pitseolak patrols for polar bears on the shores of Baffin Island, where archaeologists have discovered cordage made the Viking way (facing page) and other evidence of European contact.

Viking textiles informed her that the Canadian strands were dead ringers for yarn made by Norse women in Greenland. "That stopped me in my tracks," Sutherland recalls.

The discovery raised tantalizing questions that came to haunt Sutherland and drive more than a decade of dogged scientific sleuthing. Had a Norse party landed on the remote Baffin Island coast and made friendly contact with its native hunters? Did the yarn represent a key to a long lost chapter of New World history?

VIKING SEAFARERS were the explorers par excellence of medieval Europe. Crafting sturdy wooden sailing ships that inspire awe even today, they set sail from their Scandinavian homeland

hungering for land, gold, and treasure. Some voyaged west to what is now Scotland, England, and Ireland in the eighth century, bringing death by the sword in raids immortalized in medieval manuscripts. Many turned to foreign commerce. As early as the ninth century Viking merchants nudged eastward along the shores of the White and Black Seas and navigated the shoals of eastern European rivers. They founded cities on major Eurasian trade routes and bartered for the finest wares from the Old World—glassware from the Rhine Valley, silver from the Middle East, shells from the Red Sea, silk from China.

The most adventurous set their courses far west, into the treacherous fogbound waters of the North Atlantic. In Iceland and Greenland,

Viking colonists carved out farming settlements and filled storehouses with Arctic luxuries destined for European markets, from walrus ivory to spiraling narwhal tusks that were sold as unicorn horns. Some chieftains, fearless in the face of the unknown, pressed farther west, navigating through iceberg-strewn waters to the Americas.

Sometime between A.D. 989 and 1020, Viking seafarers—perhaps as many as 90 men and women in all—landed on a Newfoundland shore and raised three sturdy halls and an assortment of sod huts for weaving, ironworking, and ship repair. In the 1960s a Norwegian adventurer, Helge Ingstad, and his archaeologist wife, Anne Stine Ingstad, discovered and excavated the overgrown ruins of this ancient base camp at a place called L'Anse aux Meadows. Later, Canadian archaeologists found iron ship rivets and other artifacts from what appeared to be a Viking shipwreck off the coast of Ellesmere Island. But in the years that followed, few other traces of the Vikings' legendary exploration of the New World came to light—that is, until Patricia Sutherland came along.

IN THE SOFT MORNING LIGHT on Baffin Island, Sutherland and her field crew wind single file down a rocky footpath into a green hollow known as Tanfield Valley. The high wind of the previous evening has died, and the heavy clouds have cleared, leaving blue sky along the rugged coast that Viking seafarers once called Helluland—"stone slab land." Long before the Vikings arrived, the area's ancient inhabitants built a settlement here, at a site known today as Nanook.

As Sutherland clambers down the hill, she scans the shoreline warily for polar bears. The coast is clear this morning, and as she crosses between two freshwater ponds, she marvels aloud at the valley's thick, spongy moss. "It's full of greenery, full of turf for making buildings," she says. "It's the greenest valley in the area."

Sutherland, now a research fellow at the University of Aberdeen, smiles at the perfection of it all. Below us lies a protected cove, a natural harbor for an oceangoing Viking ship.

Few other traces of the Vikings' legendary exploration of the New World came to light—that is, until Patricia Sutherland came along.

Unearthing what she believes to be a Viking outpost, archaeologist Patricia Sutherland (in orange jacket) and her colleagues work in Baffin Island's Tanfield Valley, which offered turf for sod shelters and a harbor for ships.

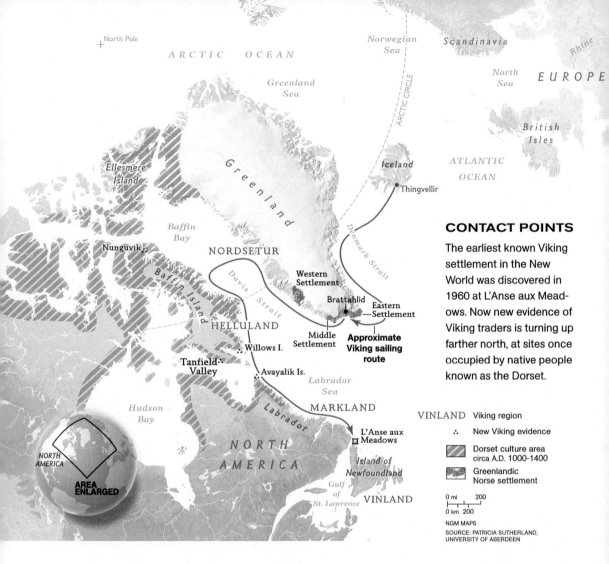

CONTACT POINTS

The earliest known Viking settlement in the New World was discovered in 1960 at L'Anse aux Meadows. Now new evidence of Viking traders is turning up farther north, at sites once occupied by native people known as the Dorset.

VINLAND — Viking region

∴ — New Viking evidence

Dorset culture area circa A.D. 1000-1400

Greenlandic Norse settlement

0 mi — 200
0 km — 200

NGM MAPS
SOURCE: PATRICIA SUTHERLAND, UNIVERSITY OF ABERDEEN

Along some boggy patches in the valley, an oily-looking microbial slick suggests the presence of bog iron, the ore that Viking smiths worked expertly. But as Sutherland scrambles up a small rise to the excavation, her high spirits evaporate. Eight inches of muddy water from the previous night's storm flood the pits. Draining them will require hours of bucket brigades and pumping. "We're running out of time here," she snaps.

With her silver-gray curls, girlish voice, and diminutive five-foot-nothing frame, Sutherland seems an unlikely expedition leader. But the 63-year-old archaeologist is a rolling storm in camp. She is the first up each morning and the last to crawl into a sleeping bag at night. In between she seems to be everywhere—flipping pancakes, making lunches for Inuit elders, checking the camp's electric bear fence. She makes nearly every decision, whether large or

small. Just three months earlier she underwent major shoulder surgery; after four weeks of excavation her left arm is so swollen that she tucks it into a sling.

But Sutherland is nothing if not determined. In 1999 the discovery of the yarn sent her back to the storage rooms at the Canadian Museum of Civilization. She began scrutinizing artifacts that other archaeologists had dug from sites of Arctic hunters known today as the Dorset, who ranged the eastern Arctic coast for nearly 2,000 years until their mysterious disappearance in the late 14th century. Poring over hundreds of presumably Dorset artifacts, often under a microscope, Sutherland discovered more pieces of spun yarn that had come from four major sites—Nunguvik, Tanfield Valley, Willows Island, and the Avayalik Islands—scattered along a thousand miles of coastline, from northern Baffin Island to

Sutherland found several carvings of what looked to be European faces, with long noses and prominent eyebrows.

northern Labrador. Sutherland also noticed something decidedly odd about the collections from these sites. Teams working there had turned up numerous pieces of wood, despite the fact that the landscape is treeless tundra. To Sutherland's astonishment, she discovered fragments of what seemed to be tally sticks, used by Vikings for recording trade transactions, and spindles, which might have been for spinning fibers. She also noted scraps of wood with square nail holes and possibly iron stains. One was radiocarbon-dated to the 14th century, toward the end of the Norse era in Greenland.

The more Sutherland sifted through the old Dorset collections, the more evidence she found that Vikings had come to these shores. While examining the stone tools, she discovered nearly 30 traditional Norse whetstones, standard gear for Viking men and women. She also found several Dorset carvings of what looked to be European faces, with long noses, prominent eyebrows, and possibly beards.

All these artifacts pointed strongly to friendly contact between Dorset hunters and Viking seafarers. But to gather more clues, Sutherland needed to excavate, and Tanfield Valley seemed the most promising of the four sites. In the 1960s American archaeologist Moreau Maxwell had dug part of a peculiar stone-and-turf structure there. The ruins, he later wrote, were "very difficult to interpret," but he finally concluded that wandering Dorset hunters had built some sort of house there. Sitting in her office, surrounded by trays of Viking artifacts, Sutherland found that hard to believe. The Dorset had built snug homes the size of an average modern bedroom. The house in Tanfield Valley, one wall of which measured more than 40 feet long, would have been much, much larger.

ON A COLD ARCTIC AFTERNOON Sutherland hunches over a square of earth inside the mysterious stone ruins. With the tip of her trowel she loosens a small piece of whale bone. Lifting the piece free, she brushes away the dirt, revealing two drill holes. The Dorset had no drills—they made holes by gouging—but Viking carpenters

Did Vikings use these notched sticks to record trade transactions? Patricia Sutherland thinks so.

stowed augers in their tool chests, and they often drilled holes for wooden dowels used to fasten pieces of wood together.

Sutherland slips the find into a plastic bag. Earlier archaeologists, she explains, excavated extensively in the ruins, so she and her colleagues must work like forensic investigators, searching for minute, overlooked clues that could shed light on Tanfield Valley's occupants. In sediments taken from inside the walls, for example, Sutherland spied several tiny pelt fragments. Expert analysis later revealed that they belonged to an Old World rat species, most probably the black rat, which must have reached the Arctic by ship.

The ruins have yielded other clues that aren't so subtle. One team member excavated a whalebone shovel closely matching those found in Greenland's Viking settlements. It's "the exact size and material as the spades used to cut sod for houses," notes Sutherland. And that makes a lot of sense. Sutherland and her colleagues found remnants of turf blocks—a material the Vikings used to build insulated walls—and a foundation made of large rocks that appear to have been cut and shaped by someone familiar with Norse stone masonry. The overall size of the

Vancouver-based Heather Pringle writes about archaeology for a variety of publications. David Coventry last photographed Panama's golden chiefs.

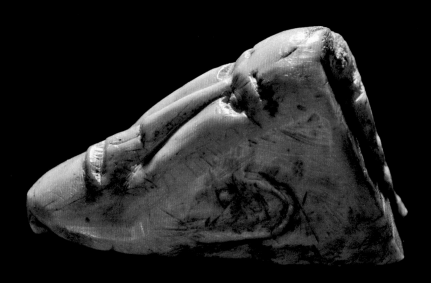

Skillfully working walrus ivory, Dorset artists portrayed the mysteries and wonders of their remote Arctic world, from wandering polar bears (below) to what may be the face of a European visitor (above). Carvings on a piece of antler (facing page) present a study in contrasts: One face is broad and round, features typical of the indigenous Dorset. The other is long and narrow with a prominent nose and heavy brows, evoking a European.

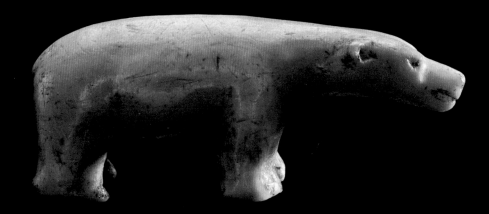

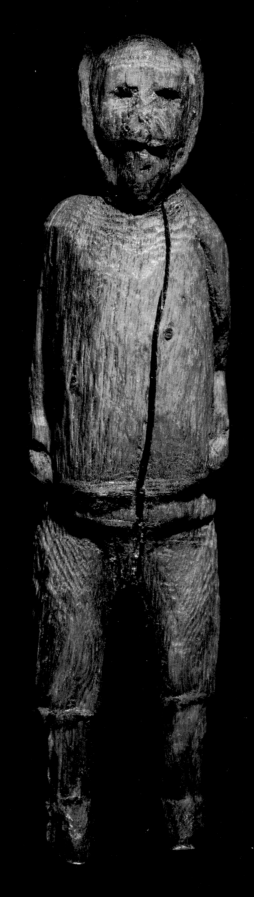

Lacking bows and arrows and living in small bands, Dorset hunters, like the one shown in this carving, likely posed little threat to the Vikings. Eventually (and mysteriously) the Dorset disappeared.

structure, the type of walls, and a drainage channel lined with stones resemble features of Viking buildings in Greenland. One area still has the telltale reek of a latrine. Along the floor, a team member excavated hand-size clumps of moss, the Viking equivalent of toilet paper. "The Dorset people were never in places long enough to build a toilet structure," says Sutherland.

But why would restless Vikings stop long enough to build on this blustery corner of Helluland? What treasures did they seek?

TOWARD THE END of the ninth century a wealthy Viking trader arrived at the court of King Alfred the Great in England. An effusive man dressed in rich, foreign attire, Ohthere told of a long voyage he had taken to the coast of the White Sea, where northerners known as the Sami had furnished him with rare Arctic luxuries, from otter and marten furs to bushels of soft bird down. Then the Viking trader presented the king with walrus ivory that could be carved into gleaming chess pieces and other exquisite works of art.

Ohthere was not the only Viking merchant who catered to the European appetite for fine goods from the frozen north. Each spring, men from Greenland's Western and Eastern Settlements went north to a rich coastal hunting ground known as Nordsetur. Camping along the shore, these medieval Greenlanders pursued walrus and other Arctic game, filling their boats with skins, furs, ivory, and even live polar bear cubs for trade abroad. Just two or three days west of Nordsetur, across the choppy waters of the Davis Strait, lay another, potentially richer Arctic treasure-house: Helluland. Its glacier-topped mountains loomed forbiddingly, but its icy waters teemed with walruses and narwhals, and its lands abounded with caribou and small fur-bearing animals.

The Viking seafarers who explored the North American coast a thousand years ago likely searched, as Ohthere did, for trading partners. In Newfoundland, a region they called Vinland, the newcomers met with a hostile reception. The aboriginal people there were well armed and viewed the foreigners as intruders on their land. But in Helluland small nomadic bands of Dorset hunters may have spotted an opportunity and rolled out the welcome mat. They had few weapons for fighting, but they excelled at hunting walruses and at trapping fur-bearing animals, whose soft hair could be spun into luxurious yarn. Moreover, some researchers think the Dorset relished trade. For hundreds of years they had bartered avidly with their aboriginal neighbors for copper and other rare goods. "They may have been the real entrepreneurs of the Arctic," says Sutherland.

With little to fear from local inhabitants, Viking seafarers evidently constructed a seasonal camp in Tanfield Valley, perhaps for hunting as well as trading. The area abounded in arctic fox, and the foreigners would have had two highly desirable goods to offer Dorset hunters for their furs: spare pieces of wood that could be carved and small chunks of metal that could be sharpened into blades. Trade in furs and other luxuries seems to have flourished. Archaeological evidence suggests that some Dorset families may have prepared animal pelts while camping a short stroll away from the Viking outpost.

Thirteen years ago, when she first spotted the curious strands of cordage, Sutherland could never have envisioned a small Viking trading post standing on the coast of her beloved Arctic. But for Sutherland much work remains. Only a small fraction of Tanfield Valley has been investigated, and Sutherland's remarkable findings—new evidence of friendly contact between Viking seafarers and aboriginal North Americans, and the discovery of what is probably the earliest European fur trade in the Americas—have stirred intense controversy among many of her colleagues. Archaeology is all about interpreting the evidence. As with the discovery of L'Anse aux Meadows decades ago, the fight for acceptance will be hard and long. But Sutherland is determined to prove the doubters wrong.

She pulls the mosquito netting over her face and resumes digging. "I think there is more to dig here, absolutely," she says with a smile. "And we are going to find much more." □

A PHOTOGRAPHER SETS OUT TO FLY
OVER THE WORLD'S MOST EXTREME DESERTS,
GUIDED BY THE SHIFTING SAND.

Sailing the Dunes

RUB AL KHALI ▪ SAUDI ARABIA Young dunes flow like calligraphy in the Rub al Khali, Arabic for Empty Quarter. Towering above them, a star dune, because of its size, will likely hold its spot for decades.

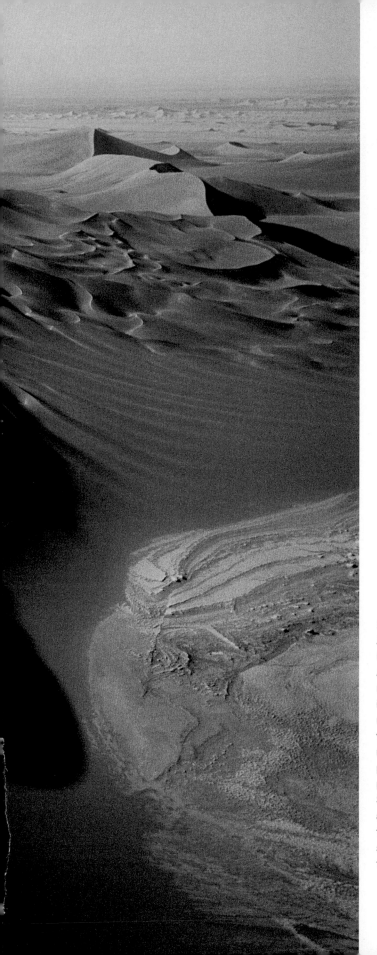

DASHT-E LUT ▪ IRAN
Aloft in a wilderness of
blowing sand, Alain
Arnoux pilots his
motorized paraglider
in tricky winds along a
massive dune in Iran's
vast Lut Desert. French-
man Arnoux, a cham-
pion flier, has assisted
photographer George
Steinmetz on more than
a dozen aerial expedi-
tions to document the
shape-shifting beauty of
the world's arid zones.

PACIFIC COAST ■ PERU Strong southerly winds fashion a chain of dunes on a remote beach in central Peru. Ocean waves supply huge amounts of the dune-building sand.

**PHOTOGRAPHS AND TEXT BY
GEORGE STEINMETZ**

I got my first lesson in the physics of sand dunes in 1998 on an expedition into the Sahara. In order to take aerial photos in this remote part

of the world, I had learned to fly a motorized paraglider, one of the lightest and slowest aircraft in the world. It weighs a little under a hundred pounds; its top airspeed is 30 miles an hour. And it has no wheels.

I mastered new skills to fly (and land) the paraglider. But there was one I hadn't realized I'd need to survive the Sahara: reading sand dunes. Just as the sailor watches whitecaps for the sudden squall, I had to learn to anticipate the invisible currents of air that created the dunes. If I wasn't paying attention, I could get caught in turbulence—or even a fatal downdraft.

The Sahara is traversed by endless rows of dunes called barchans. The word means "crescent-shaped dune" in the Turkic languages of eastern Europe and Central and northern Asia. I had become intrigued with them while reading a book by Ralph Bagnold, a British Army officer who pioneered motorized travel in the Libyan Desert in the 1920s and '30s. Bagnold described barchans as life-forms—they move, multiply, maintain structure, and adapt to their environment. I thought they might be interesting to photograph from above.

But first I had to reach the dunes. I traveled to the region with France's Alain Arnoux, a champion of motorized paragliding. I was counting on him to help me fly safely. Getting to the barchans took us four days in a four-wheel drive, traveling from N'Djamena, the capital of Chad, to the far north. The sand that makes up the dunes had traveled too, migrating west from Egypt and Sudan. We were guided by an

BADAIN JARAN ▪ **CHINA** Improbable jewel-bright lakes nestle among thousand-foot-high star dunes in a desert where Mongolian goat and sheep herders live. They depend on the springs that feed these salt lakes.

old French map that depicted the dunes as right parentheses, all pointing into the wind.

I did not realize the difficulties that awaited. Nor did I realize the allure of dunes. Once I started flying in the desert, I came under its spell and began what turned out to be a 15-year project to photograph the world's most extreme deserts.

When we got to the Mourdi Depression, my traveling companion had bad news. Shouting to be heard over the gale, Alain told me there was no way even he could fly in such wind. So we drove out into the middle of the broad stony basin until we found a 50-foot-tall barchan to give us some shelter for the night.

We awoke before dawn. The wind on the dune crest had died down to a breeze. I took off at sunrise, running down the windward slope of the dune. After gaining 500 feet, I felt like an insect flying over an enormous conveyor belt in a croissant factory. The barchans stretched to the horizon as they combined, separated, and spawned progeny.

I soon became nervous. The wind was much faster than I was, so I was being pushed backward while heading into it. It was like trying to swim up a river against a current that's moving faster than you can swim. That's a frightening experience for a pilot. You can't see what's behind you, and when you land, you have a hundred pounds on your back and a large sail over your head that wants to keep moving backward.

Ground friction slows the wind, especially in the morning, so I dropped to within 50 feet of the dune crests to advance. After an hour even the wind down low began to increase and become turbulent. The sun was heating up the dark ground, creating bubbles of rising hot air that broke up the smooth flow of wind across the surface. When I gained altitude to find our dune camp, I began flying with the wind instead of against it and suddenly found myself moving ahead at more than 70 miles an hour—an alarming speed. I turned into the wind and

George Steinmetz is the author of the new book Desert Air, *featuring photos of extreme deserts made while he soars in his "flying lawn chair."*

hovered like a kite 200 feet above camp. Alain came zooming in underneath me. Landing in such a gale made me anxious, and I watched to see what the champion would do.

He read the dune like an open book: The wind was rushing over the top of its crest and then doubling back. To try and land near our cars, parked in the dune's inner arc, would be fatal. The paraglider is an inflated wing; in turbulent air it could lose rigidity and crumple. Landing on the dune's windward slope was a better option, but a gust could push us back into the whirlpool of wind—and a nasty mess. As I watched, Alain made the prudent choice and landed in the gravel plains beside the dune, avoiding the turbulence. I soon came down to join him.

Alain had given me a great lesson in reading the winds. After 26 desert flying expeditions, I've had a lot of postgraduate training. I have found that dunes are both flyable and beautiful in the calm first hours of morning.

And I've learned to be patient and to pick my seasons carefully. In the Sahara, for example, fall is best because the winds are relatively light and the weather is cool.

I still fear sandstorms, which can come up with little notice. I've even learned how to land in them: as soon and as quickly as possible. With an aircraft that flies faster than I can run, I have also learned that dunes are my friends. They're soft and always point the direction to a safe landing. You don't need a weatherman to know which way the wind blows when you have dunes to inform you.

I have developed a few simple rules. The smallest dunes are the ones most affected by the wind, so their direction indicates the way the wind is blowing. If at all possible, land on the sunny side of a sand dune; the shady side usually has downdrafts, so you just drop like a stone. White sand is safer to fly over than dark sand. Dark sand absorbs the heat, then releases it in big bubbles of hot air, like a lava lamp. When the sand is blowing off the dune crests, it's a good time to be on the ground. And last, it's always better to be on the ground wishing you were in the sky than in the sky wishing you were on the ground. ☐

Sand Dune Formation

Covering some 20 percent of the world's deserts, dunes form wherever there's constant wind and loose sand. Size depends on the supply of available sand; shapes follow the dictates of wind direction.

Barchan

"Barchan" is Turkic for a crescent-shaped dune—found on the edge of sand seas and formed when the wind blows steadily from one direction.

Unidirectional winds

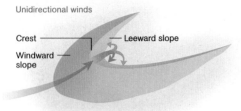

Crest — Leeward slope

Windward slope

PACIFIC COAST, PERU

Seif

Elongated, sharp-crested seifs, named after the Arabic word for sword, take shape in regions with moderate sand and shifting winds.

Slightly variable winds

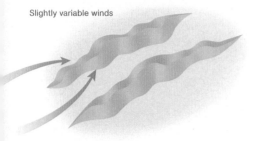

SAHARA, CHAD

Star Dune

Seasonally changing winds create multiarmed, pyramid-shaped dunes. Building up more than out, they can rise to over a thousand feet.

Multidirectional winds

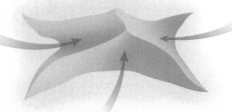

RUB AL KHALI, SAUDI ARABIA

GRAPHICS: LAWSON PARKER, NGM STAFF

WADI HAZAR ▪ YEMEN Giant dunes appear to be crumbling
into pieces, a puzzling phenomenon in the region's Empty Quarter.
A change in wind patterns may explain the desert redesign.

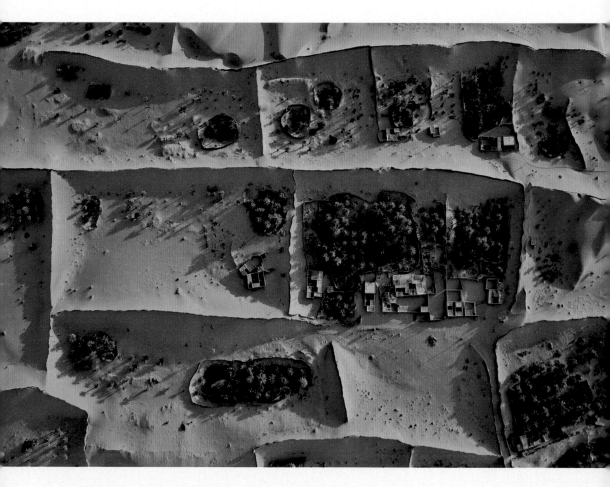

SAHARA ▪ ALGERIA Villagers in an oasis near Timimoun erect fences made of palm fronds to protect their gardens from the shifting sand, which settles near the fences as the wind blows.

NAMIB DESERT ▪ NAMIBIA Sand repossesses buildings in Kolmanskop, a diamond-mining town abandoned in the 1950s. The ruins sit near an active sand stream that may someday bury them.

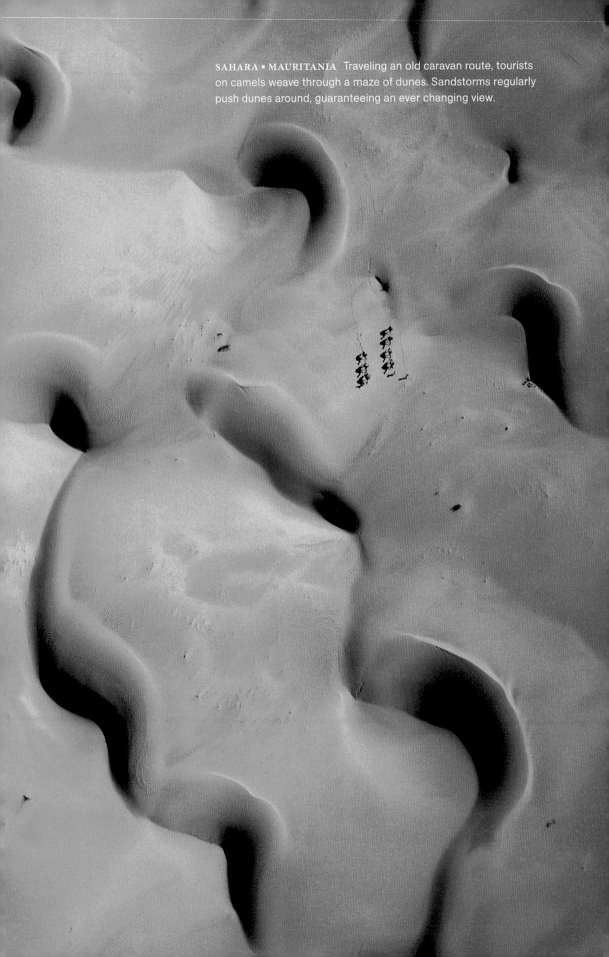

SAHARA ▪ MAURITANIA Traveling an old caravan route, tourists on camels weave through a maze of dunes. Sandstorms regularly push dunes around, guaranteeing an ever changing view.

A hidden camera captures a fleeting glimpse of an Asiatic cheetah. Only a few dozen survive in a remote corner of Iran. Worldwide cheetah numbers have plunged from an estimated 100,000 in 1900 to fewer than 10,000 today.

CHEETAHS
ON
THE EDGE

Most vulnerable of the world's big cats, cheetahs are also one of its shrewdest survivors.

By Roff Smith

Photographs by Frans Lanting

Anticipation ripples through the crowd. Fingers tighten around binoculars. Camera lenses snap into focus. No fewer than 11 canopied safari buses, bright with tourists and bristling with long lenses, huddle near a solitary acacia tree in Tanzania's Serengeti National Park. For the past half hour a mother cheetah named Etta has been sitting in the shade with her four young cubs, eyeing a herd of Thomson's gazelles that drifted into view on a nearby rise. Now she's up and moving, sidling toward the herd with a studied nonchalance that fools no one, least of all the gazelles, which are staring nervously in her direction.

Suddenly one of the guides shouts, as the gazelles break and run and Etta launches into an explosive sprint. The sleek cat is too fast for the eye to follow, blurring through the grass like a bullet. The drama is over in seconds, ending with a puff of dust and a stranglehold on a luckless young gazelle. As Etta drags the carcass back to her cubs, they emerge from the scrub eager to tuck into the feast. The safari buses are only seconds behind, the drivers jockeying to get the best camera angles for their customers.

Cheetahs have come to occupy a curious place in the human imagination. Beautiful and exotic, sports car fast and famously docile, they are as much media stars as denizens of the wild, darlings of filmmakers and advertisers the world over. Tap "cheetah" and "images" into your computer's search bar, and more than 20 million results pop up—from fashion shoots to flashy

car ads to photos of pet cheetahs riding in the backseats of Mercedes convertibles.

All this pop culture presence might create the impression that cheetahs are as secure in nature as they are in the popular imagination. They are not. In fact, cheetahs are the most vulnerable of the world's big cats, surprisingly rare and growing steadily rarer. A few centuries ago cheetahs roamed from the Indian subcontinent to the shores of the Red Sea and throughout much of Africa. As fleet of foot as they are, though, they couldn't outrun the long reach of humanity. Today the Asiatic cheetah, the elegant subspecies that once graced the royal courts of India, Persia,

---

Roff Smith wrote about Australia's Fraser Island in September 2010. Frans Lanting has documented wildlife from the Amazon to Antarctica.

A nearly grown cheetah cub picks its way through a maze of safari vans in Kenya's Masai Mara National Reserve. Tourism, lions, and encroaching herds of cattle all add to the challenges of growing up on the African grasslands. Mortality rates for cheetah cubs can run as high as 95 percent.

and Arabia, is all but extinct. In Africa cheetah numbers plummeted by more than 90 percent during the course of the 20th century, as farmers, ranchers, and herdsmen crowded the cats out of their habitat, hunters shot them for sport, and poachers captured cubs for the lucrative trade in exotic pets. In all, fewer than 10,000 cheetahs survive in the wild today.

Even within Africa's great game parks, cheetahs are under heavy pressure. Shy and delicately built, the only big cats that cannot roar, they are bullied into the margins by lions, which are far stronger both in body and number. Consider Tanzania's Serengeti National Park and the adjoining Masai Mara National Reserve in Kenya. Taken together the two parks are home to more than 3,000 lions, an estimated 1,000 leopards, and a mere 300 cheetahs. And despite their celebrity status, cheetahs lose out to lions in the tourism stakes as well. "Cheetahs tend to be something people look for on their second safari," says guide Eliyahu Eliyahu. "The first time around is all about seeing lions. The trouble is, where you have a big lion population, you will never have many cheetahs."

IF CHEETAHS SEEM a breed apart, it's because they are. Not only are they a separate species

Cheetahs remain highly fashionable in Saudi Arabia and the Gulf states. "A rich, young man buys himself a cheetah to go with his sports car. It's typically a new-money thing."
—Mordecai Ogada

from the other great cats, but they belong to a separate genus as well, a genus with just one member: themselves. Their genus name, *Acinonyx,* comes from Greek words for "thorn" and "claw" and refers to the cheetah's curious semi-retractable claw, a feature they share with no other cat. Unlike lions and leopards, whose fully retractable claws are tools designed for tearing flesh and climbing trees, cheetahs have claws that are more like the spikes on a sprinter's track shoe and serve a similar function: solid grip and quick acceleration.

Everything about a cheetah is designed for speed—pure, raw, explosive speed. Put a cheetah and a Lamborghini side by side on a freeway, and it will be an even-money bet which will smash the speed limit first. Both can do zero to 60 in under three seconds, but the cheetah can crack 45 miles an hour in the first couple of strides. And what strides. Thanks to its flexible spine and long, fluid legs, a cheetah can gobble up turf in bounds that exceed 25 feet. An elite human athlete who could leap that far even once, after a good run, would be well on his or her way to qualifying for the Olympic Games. A cheetah sprinting at top speed might be doing that up to four times a second.

Such superhuman abilities lent cheetahs an otherworldly aura in ancient times. Egyptians were the first people to tame them as pets and immortalize them in images on tombs and temples, nearly 4,000 years ago. In India, Iran, and Arabia, coursing with cheetahs—or "hunting leopards," as they were known—became an immensely popular sport among the aristocracy. In the courts of the Mogul emperors, cheetahs became a kind of motif, celebrated in paintings and tapestries, folklore and verse. Favorite cheetahs were adorned with jeweled collars and featured prominently in royal processions.

Cheetahs remain highly fashionable in Saudi Arabia and the Gulf states, where a cub can fetch upwards of $10,000. "A rich, young man buys himself a cheetah to go with his sports car," says Mordecai Ogada, a Kenyan wildlife biologist who has studied cheetah-human relationships and wildlife trafficking. "It's typically a new-money thing nowadays."

Rescued as a cub from the hands of a poacher, five-year-old Koshki grew up in a reserve in northeast Iran. He's one of only two Asiatic cheetahs living in captivity. A thick tuft of fur on his shoulders, needed for bitter winters on the high steppes of central Iran, sets him apart from African cheetahs.

In places such as the United Arab Emirates cheetahs occupy a kind of legal limbo. "The importation is clandestine," says Ogada, "but once there, the trade is open. Trafficked cheetahs can easily be 'laundered' and made to appear as though they were legally bred in captivity. It's difficult to determine the source of cubs unless you do genetic analysis and identify them as members of a subspecies that's endemic to a particular area."

How great a toll trafficking is taking on the world's dwindling cheetah population is anyone's guess, but evidence suggests that trade in wild cheetah cubs is a large-scale enterprise. Even a cursory trawl of the Internet turns up plenty of cubs being offered for sale by "breeders" in places like Dubai. Several cheetah smugglers were arrested last year in Tanzania and Kenya, and there were rumors of cheetah cubs being offered for sale as far afield as Cameroon.

"I suspect the problem is bigger than we imagine," says Yeneneh Teka, head of Ethiopia's Wildlife Development and Protection Directorate. "There is a great deal of money involved, and like the people who are smuggling drugs and guns, those who smuggle wildlife have well-established networks."

Last year Ethiopian authorities cracked down

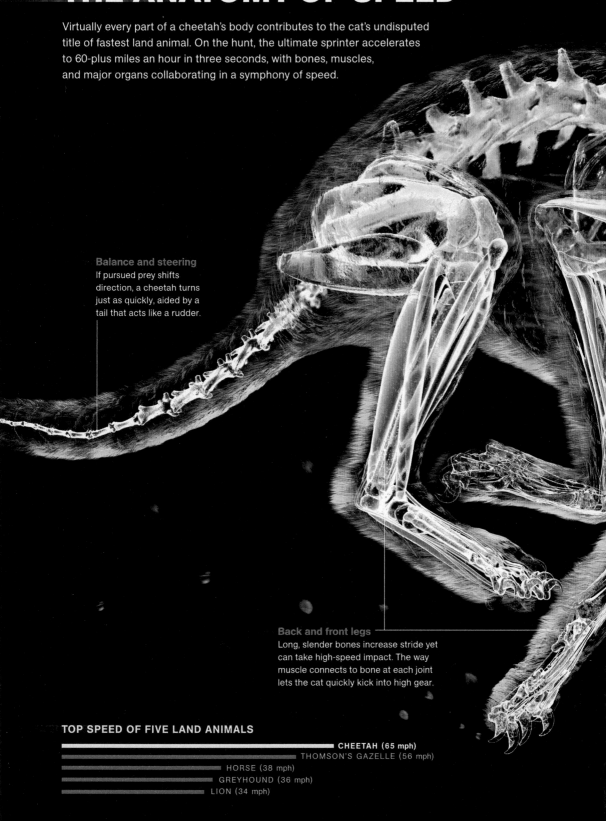

THE ANATOMY OF SPEED

Virtually every part of a cheetah's body contributes to the cat's undisputed title of fastest land animal. On the hunt, the ultimate sprinter accelerates to 60-plus miles an hour in three seconds, with bones, muscles, and major organs collaborating in a symphony of speed.

Balance and steering
If pursued prey shifts direction, a cheetah turns just as quickly, aided by a tail that acts like a rudder.

Back and front legs
Long, slender bones increase stride yet can take high-speed impact. The way muscle connects to bone at each joint lets the cat quickly kick into high gear.

TOP SPEED OF FIVE LAND ANIMALS

CHEETAH (65 mph)
THOMSON'S GAZELLE (56 mph)
HORSE (38 mph)
GREYHOUND (36 mph)
LION (34 mph)

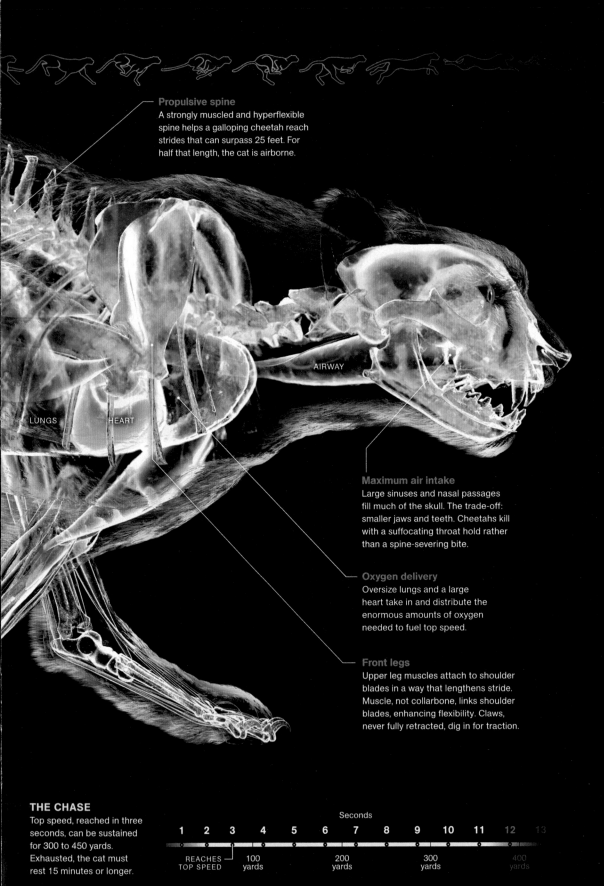

Propulsive spine
A strongly muscled and hyperflexible spine helps a galloping cheetah reach strides that can surpass 25 feet. For half that length, the cat is airborne.

AIRWAY

LUNGS   HEART

Maximum air intake
Large sinuses and nasal passages fill much of the skull. The trade-off: smaller jaws and teeth. Cheetahs kill with a suffocating throat hold rather than a spine-severing bite.

Oxygen delivery
Oversize lungs and a large heart take in and distribute the enormous amounts of oxygen needed to fuel top speed.

Front legs
Upper leg muscles attach to shoulder blades in a way that lengthens stride. Muscle, not collarbone, links shoulder blades, enhancing flexibility. Claws, never fully retracted, dig in for traction.

THE CHASE
Top speed, reached in three seconds, can be sustained for 300 to 450 yards. Exhausted, the cat must rest 15 minutes or longer.

Seconds

1   2   3   4   5   6   7   8   9   10   11   12   13

REACHES   100   200   300   400
TOP SPEED   yards   yards   yards   yards

JASON TREAT, NGM STAFF. ART: BRYAN CHRISTIE. SOURCES: KRISTOFER M. HELGEN, MATTHEW W. TOCHERI, E. GRACE VEATCH, KATHRYN J. MCGRATH, NATIONAL MUSEUM OF NATURAL HISTORY, SMITHSONIAN INSTITUTION; PENNY HUDSON, ROYAL VETERINARY COLLEGE

One supermom is known to have mothered at least 10 percent of all the adult cheetahs in the southern Serengeti. No other carnivore "relies so heavily on the success of so few females."
—Sarah Durant

on wildlife smuggling and instituted a training program for border guards and customs officials. The stepped-up enforcement paid off when officials intercepted a consignment of cheetah cubs as they were being smuggled into Somalia.

"While the border guards were examining the truck's paperwork, they heard scratching sounds coming from a jerry can that was supposed to be full of petrol," Teka says. "When they opened it up, they found five tiny cheetah cubs in very poor condition." One of the cubs died. The other four, after weeks of veterinary care, were taken to a wildlife sanctuary operated by the Born Free Foundation an hour north of Addis Ababa, where they will spend the rest of their lives. Although it's a happy ending for the four survivors, it's a net loss for the species.

"They'll never be able to return to the wild," says Ogada. "Even if you could teach them to hunt, humans can't teach cubs how to recognize and avoid predators such as lions and hyenas." And although some cheetahs have been successfully rewilded on large, fenced reserves in South Africa, the wide-open grasslands are a far more dangerous place to grow up. Orphaned cubs "wouldn't stand a chance in a place like the Serengeti," says Ogada.

Even mother cheetahs find it difficult to raise cubs in the wild, where mortality among cubs can run as high as 95 percent. The great majority of cubs may never make it out of the den in which they're born. They're killed in raids by lions or hyenas, or they die of exposure, or they're abandoned by mothers that aren't skillful

enough hunters to support them. Indeed, many female cheetahs go their entire lives without raising a single cub to maturity.

THERE ARE A RARE FEW, however, that somehow manage to beat the odds and enjoy astonishing success in raising cubs, some even fostering the offspring of other females. Superb hunters and wise in the ways of the bush, these supermoms manage to make a kill nearly every day while keeping their brood safe on the wide-open stage of the African grasslands, beneath the very noses of lions and hyenas. One such supermom, a seven-year-old named Eleanor, is known to have mothered at least 10 percent of all the adult cheetahs in the southern Serengeti.

"I'm not aware of any other carnivore whose survival relies so heavily on the success of so few females," says Sarah Durant of the Zoological Society of London. Durant directs the Serengeti Cheetah Project, one of the world's longest running carnivore studies. Now in its 38th year, the project has chronicled the lives and maternal pedigrees of generations of the Serengeti's cheetahs. It is hot, dusty work, involving long hours bouncing over the grasslands in hard-bitten Land Rovers seeking out the most elusive of Africa's great cats. It was Durant's painstaking research that revealed the vital importance of supermoms.

Though the matriarchal lines of the Serengeti's cheetah population are now well documented, paternity is another matter. Wildlife biologist Helen O'Neill waits patiently in her Land Rover a short distance from where three cheetah brothers—Mocha, Latte, and Espresso, known collectively as the Coffee Boys—lie sprawled in the shade of a ballanite tree. O'Neill is on what is delicately referred to as "poop patrol," collecting feces dropped by specific, identifiable cheetahs. Scientists at the Zoological Society of London are able to extract DNA samples and hope to fill in the paternal side of the Serengeti's family trees.

Analysis so far suggests that cheetah females are far more promiscuous than anyone suspected: In as many as half their litters, the cubs have different fathers. "We suspect this kind of multiple mating could have genetic benefits in

A 7.19 second dash

That's all it took for Tommy T to cover 100 meters in a timed run at the Cincinnati Zoo. (A half second of his run is shown here.) Sarah, the fastest cheetah ever clocked, finished in 5.95. By comparison, Olympian Usain Bolt's record is 9.58.

Cinematography by Greg Wilson

 An ultra-high-speed camera recorded this cheetah's run in rich detail. See the video on our iPad and Kindle Fire editions.

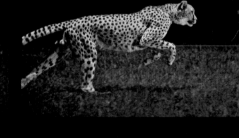

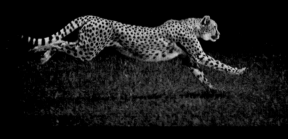

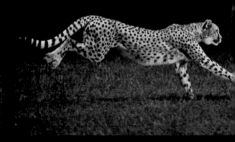

PHANTOM CAMERA TECHNICIAN: EDWARD RICHARDSON. CAMERA OPERATORS: FRANK BUONO, SCOTT DROPKIN. GAFFER: MIKE GERZEVITZ. KEY GRIP: TRAVIS TIPS. WINCH OPERATORS

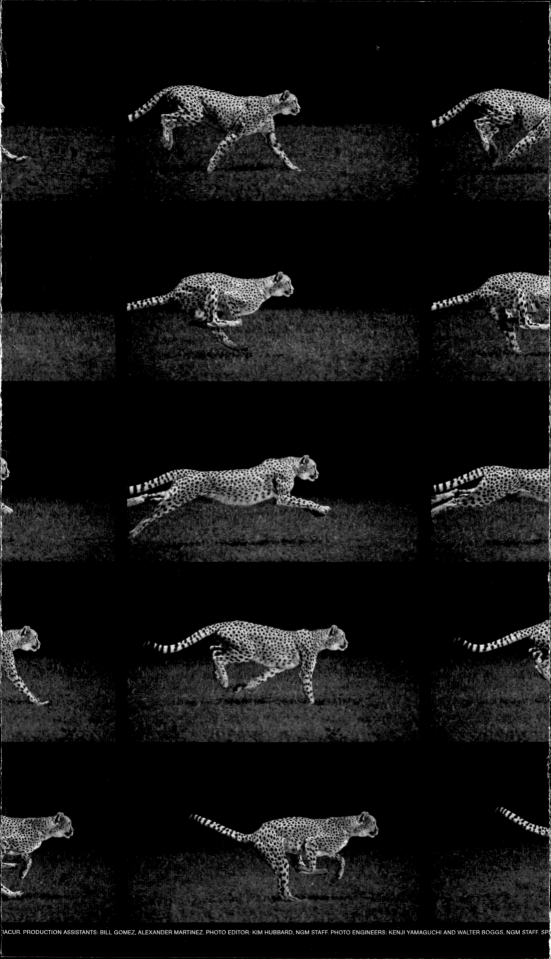

IACUR. PRODUCTION ASSISTANTS: BILL GOMEZ, ALEXANDER MARTINEZ. PHOTO EDITOR: KIM HUBBARD, NGM STAFF. PHOTO ENGINEERS: KENJI YAMAGUCHI AND WALTER BOGGS, NGM STAFF. SP

Traveling at 100 feet per second, a young male cheetah is airborne at the Cincinnati Zoo. In a single stride the agile cat strikes one paw after another on the ground, lifts completely into the air, and covers nearly 25 feet.

 See cheetahs in action and learn the secrets of their speed on your tablet.

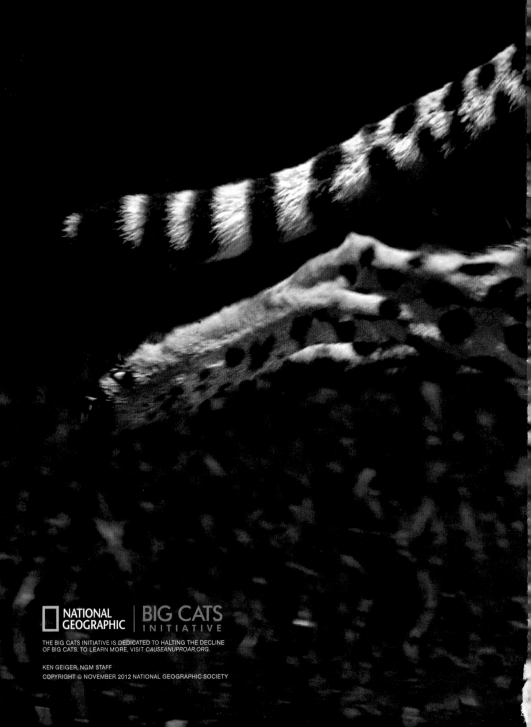

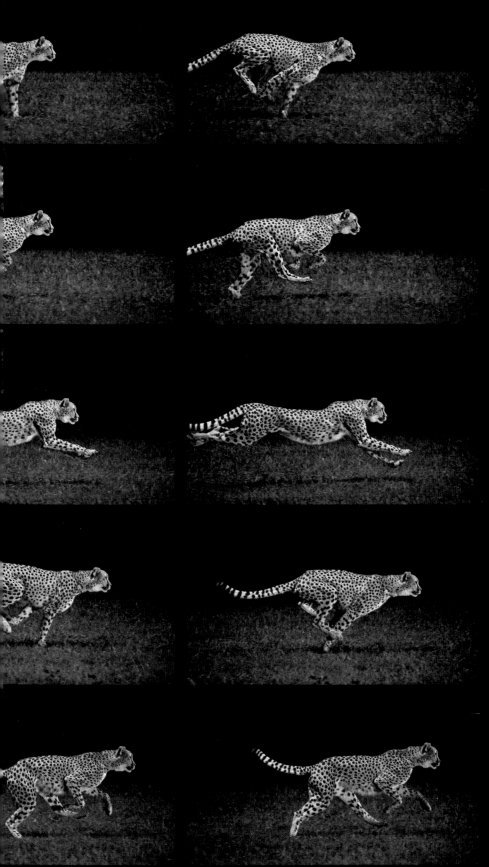

CIAL THANKS TO CINCINNATI ZOO & BOTANICAL GARDEN AND MIAMI TOWNSHIP FIRE DEPARTMENT

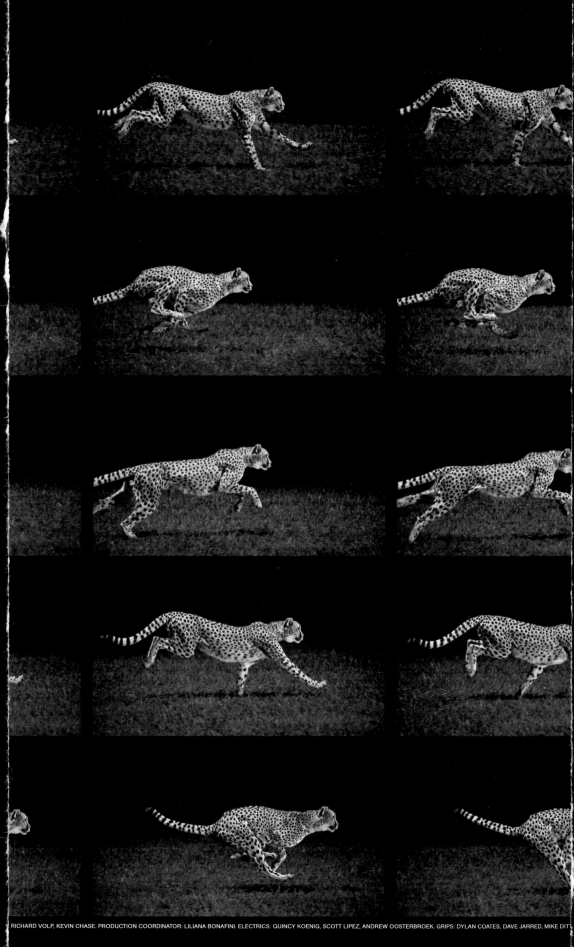

RICHARD VOLP, KEVIN CHASE. PRODUCTION COORDINATOR: LILIANA BONAFINI. ELECTRICS: QUINCY KOENIG, SCOTT LIPEZ, ANDREW OOSTERBROEK. GRIPS: DYLAN COATES, DAVE JARRED, MIKE DIT

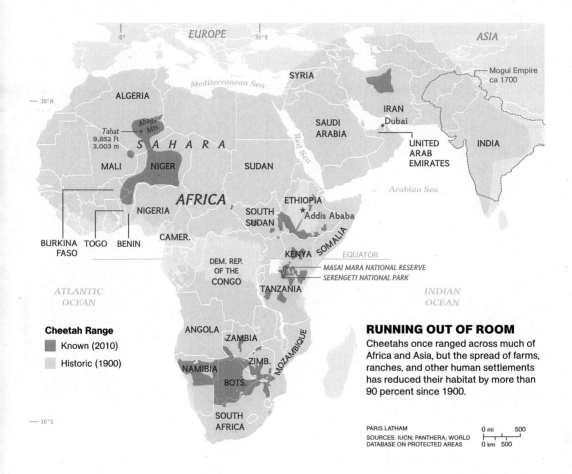

Cheetah Range

- Known (2010)
- Historic (1900)

RUNNING OUT OF ROOM

Cheetahs once ranged across much of Africa and Asia, but the spread of farms, ranches, and other human settlements has reduced their habitat by more than 90 percent since 1900.

PARIS LATHAM
SOURCES: IUCN; PANTHERA; WORLD DATABASE ON PROTECTED AREAS

0 mi 500
0 km 500

an uncertain environment," says Durant. "Think of it as bet hedging by the cheetah mothers to try to ensure that some of their progeny survive."

A WORLD AWAY FROM the sunlit grasslands of the Serengeti, late on a cold, clear winter's afternoon, a lone male cheetah picks his way along a snow-dusted ridgeline. He pauses briefly to scent mark a tamarisk tree, then slinks out of view of the remotely operated video camera that has been recording his passage.

The concealed camera is one of 80 camera traps that have been deployed around the Dasht-e Kavir, a remote region in Iran's mountainous central plateau, in the hopes of glimpsing one of the world's rarest and most elusive big cats: the Asiatic cheetah.

"It's like a dream come true when we get something like this," says Iranian wildlife biologist Houman Jowkar of the 27 seconds of footage. Jowkar is with the Conservation of the Asiatic Cheetah Project, which was set up by Iran's Department of Environment in 2001 in a bid to save the last remaining population of these endangered cheetahs. "These cats are incredibly rare," says Jowkar. "We have game wardens who have lived and worked in these mountains for years but have never seen a live cheetah."

The camera-trap program has helped Iranian scientists determine roughly how many cheetahs are left and where they live—vital information for developing a conservation strategy. "We're lucky these beautiful cats are spotted," Jowkar says. "By using their unique coat

> **"Cheetahs have not been pushed into these mountains recently. They've been here for thousands of years. People don't realize how tough and versatile cheetahs really are."**
> *—Luke Hunter*

patterns, we can identify them individually and work out their population and distribution."

All the same, saving the Asiatic cheetah will be a tall order. Its downfall traces back to the glory days of the Mogul Empire, when hunting with cheetahs became all the rage. One Mogul emperor is said to have collected more than 9,000 cheetahs during his 49-year reign.

Compare then and now. In ten years of setting out scores of cameras, Iranian researchers have so far managed to obtain a mere 192 fleeting images. Those images document 76 gaunt individuals, pretty much all that remains of a noble subspecies of cheetah that once roamed throughout much of Asia. Today's survivors eke out a precarious existence. Stalking antelope and mountain sheep on steep, stony slopes, they compete with wolves and even humans, for whom gazelles and sheep are also a handy food source.

"They are living on a knife edge, at the very limit of what is ecologically possible," says Luke Hunter, president of Panthera, an international conservation group dedicated to preserving big cats, and a collaborator on the Iranian cheetah project. "What's intriguing, though, is that these cheetahs have not been pushed into these mountains recently. They've been here for thousands of years. People don't realize how tough and versatile cheetahs really are."

Indeed they are. Despite their vulnerability, cheetahs are one of the world's hardiest and shrewdest survivors, enduring both the bitter winters of the Iranian steppes and the scorching heat of the Sahara wadis. "They are not just fast," says Algerian wildlife biologist Farid Belbachir, who has been setting camera traps in Algeria's Ahaggar Mountains, trying to capture images of the critically endangered Saharan cheetah. "They understand the landscape. They've figured out how to use the narrow parts of the wadis to launch their attacks, to give their prey less opportunity to escape."

BACK IN SERENGETI National Park, it's now in the shank of the afternoon, with the hot taste of dust in the air and thunderheads tumbling and billowing along the horizon. For the past hour or so Etta has been creeping up on a big male

A young cheetah mother named Etta by researchers scans the Serengeti for signs of danger while her four 12-week-old cubs wrestle. A long-running study has found that the majority of cubs here are raised by a small group of cheetah supermoms.

gazelle, drawing to within 40 yards of him, while he has remained oblivious to her presence.

"It's too early to tell if Etta is going to turn out to be a supermum," Durant says. "This is only her first litter. But the fact that she has brought four cubs out of the den and has raised them this far is an encouraging sign."

The gazelle is big and healthy, with a lot of meat on him. Etta takes another couple of quick, furtive steps forward, then crouches and waits, looking like a sprinter on the starting blocks, poised and ready for the gun.

A tense minute crawls by, then another. Suddenly, and seemingly for no reason at all, Etta just stands up and strolls away. Something doesn't feel right to her—a whiff of hyena on the breeze or maybe the scent of lions. Whatever it is, to a mother of four young cubs alone on the Serengeti, one fat gazelle isn't worth the risk. She beckons to her cubs to come along, and together they trot off into the violet haze. □

BIG CAT WEEK

In support of National Geographic's Big Cats Initiative, **Nat Geo WILD** presents a week of exotic felines. Prime time in December; check local listings.

A male cheetah assumes a lookout pose in a fig tree in Kenya's Masai Mara National Reserve. His prospects are sobering. Shy and aloof by nature, requiring vast spaces to live and hunt, the planet's fastest sprinters are in a race for their very survival.

A TRACTOR ROAD MUDDIED BY AUTUMN RAIN IN LEE COUNTY

RETURN TO THE
ARKANSAS DELTA

The delta west of the Mississippi River was once a place where sharecroppers lived in segregation and poverty yet forged a vibrant community. Industrial farming has erased their culture, leaving behind endless sky and few people. Eugene Richards documented their world four decades ago. Now he returns to where his pictures began.

By **Charles Bowden**

Photographs and Captions by **Eugene Richards**

A flashback strikes, and the photographer is once again walking across the field as our car drives down the two-lane road in the Arkansas Delta. "It had to have happened close to here," he says, and looks out the car window with sad eyes. Beyond the plowed ground are the remains of a sharecropper's shack that has been made irrelevant by the mechanical revolution of the past 70 years. "I'm walking with Dorothea across a plowed field to visit some people who lived in that shack," he says in his soft voice. "And then a crop duster sees me, sweeps down, and empties his tank of chemicals on us. She really gets drenched."

He stops. The woman who was with him at that moment became his wife. She later got breast cancer, and he always wondered if that shower of chemicals had something to do with it. The sun is bright, wisteria gone wild is climbing roadside trees, its lavender flowers hanging 40 feet in the air. The air is fresh with April, a hint of rain, and the stands of forest roar with spring. At dawn low clouds scud over the land, then the sun comes on, and the world begins again.

"That's it. That's all I can remember about that day."

The photographer is a white man who had come from Boston to the small town of Augusta during the civil rights era of the late sixties, and he now believes it was the most important time of his life. He was with VISTA (Volunteers in Service to America), working in a day-care center for black and white kids, and it wasn't long before his presence seemed to unsettle the white population of the town. His name is Eugene Richards, and because of an incident one night all those years ago, much about those days and nights is beyond his reach.

Memory comes and goes here on the delta, mainly goes.

THE ARKANSAS DELTA IS A SERIES OF RIVER basins that empty into the Mississippi from the west: the St. Francis, the White, and the Arkansas. Various agricultural systems have been tried here—slavery, sharecropping, industrial farming—all producing wealth for a handful amid widespread poverty. The ancient forests have been cut, many towns have dwindled into ghosts, and yet there is this one thing: The place still beckons, captures the heart, and persists like the blues songs that grew out of the pain and the rough-edged Saturday nights.

There are soft reasons for hope on the delta: the sentimental tug of the light at dawn, the scent of violent growth in the remaining woods, the lazy movement of the rivers across the pan of dirt. But none of this makes up for a hard history of poverty, lynchings, and an out-migration into cities because of a rejection by the delta itself.

The delta is the soul of the South, a place always becoming a New South and yet always shrouded in its past, a place that gave the nation the blues and harbored the Ku Klux Klan and in the sixties was a cauldron of social change that boiled up in young black people and spilled over to young white people all across the country.

1970: I photographed the Landers sisters on the steps of Mount Calver Baptist Church of Christ, the makeshift chapel built by their preacher father in a shack in Rawlinson.

Now it is a vast agricultural machine that has swept clean the land, that seems to hardly need people or towns.

Eugene Richards falls silent. We drive on. The flashback fades, the land remains, the place of the great river and the phantom chords of American memory.

THE SOIL HERE IS SOME OF THE MOST FERTILE in the world, but that has not been enough. Sixty million years ago the Gulf of Mexico extended all the way to Missouri. As the sea gradually withdrew, multiple rivers remained, including the Mississippi and its tributaries, which laid down deposits of deep soil, richer than dreams. Some 12,000 years ago the Ice Age ended, the glaciers melted, the rivers rose, and then came flood after flood, blanketing the delta of the mighty Mississippi. Annual flooding continued to build up the region's loamy, alluvial deposits, which measure a hundred feet deep in places.

American settlers arrived in the Arkansas Delta around 1800 and confronted a place of forbidding forests amid swamps, a different landscape from what you see today. A few decades later, as forests were cleared and swamps

drained, the delta became a promised land. The plantation system took hold, though Arkansas generally lacks the big Greek Revival mansions of the movies. There simply wasn't enough time: The big plantation houses were just getting built here when the Civil War changed everything.

This chapter of Arkansas Delta history is written on the streets of Cotton Plant, a town of 649 people. In 1846 a man named William Lynch came over from Mississippi, threw up a house and store, and tried growing something relatively new for these parts. King Cotton began its reign. By then the Arkansas Delta was experiencing a period of dramatic growth. Steamboats on the Arkansas rivers could easily transport cotton to markets down in New Orleans. The state's estimated annual per capita income was $68—three dollars more than the national average. Slavery is what made the growth possible. By the outbreak of the Civil War some delta counties had more blacks than whites.

Today on Cotton Plant's main street the old Presbyterian church melts like wax in the sun. In front of the police station are two public benches, both chained. Old men sit in the shade by the dead downtown. "There used to be a veneer

1970: A young marine home on leave stood at attention in front of a sharecropper shack where a field worker lived with his blind wife and two blind sons.

The Elaine massacre is one of the largest race killings of blacks in U.S. history, but few have heard of it. The past can be forgotten but not erased.

plant, and it ran 24 hours a day," one old man told me. "Now everyone that works has to go somewhere else."

I AM SEARCHING FOR THE SITE OF THE ELAINE massacre, an event that began in a hamlet called Hoop Spur, three miles from the town of Elaine. In late September 1919 black sharecroppers held a meeting at a church in Hoop Spur to discuss how to get better prices for their cotton. The emancipation of slaves had destroyed the plantations' source of free labor and replaced it with the sharecropper system. After the Civil War newly freed slaves thought they could work as tenant farmers here and escape the repression of Dixie. That worked for a while.

There was gunfire at the sharecropper meeting,

and when it ended, a deputy sheriff was wounded and a railroad security officer was dead. For days afterward mobs of whites roamed with guns and hunted blacks in the thickets. U.S. Army troops were called in and may also have done some killing. Whites called it a black insurrection; blacks called it a massacre by whites. No one agrees on the tallies. Perhaps five whites were killed. Estimates run from 20 into the hundreds of black men, women, and children dead. The bottom line: This is one of the largest race killings of blacks in U.S. history, but most people today have never heard of it. I stand in a field where Hoop Spur used to be. There are only plowed ground and rows of plants. Nothing in the fringe of trees tells tales of those days.

Maybe that is best. Things move on. Or maybe the past can be forgotten but not erased.

THE SLAUGHTER OF THE FORESTS ON THE Arkansas side of the Mississippi River lagged behind the felling of ancient hardwoods on the

---

Charles Bowden recorded oral histories in the Mississippi Delta in 1968, just miles from where Eugene Richards worked in Arkansas.

1971: On a freezing Saturday morning the Valentine children watched TV, though the plastic and cardboard on the windows barely kept out the wind and cold.

east side. Not until the early 20th century did lumbering turn the delta into a moonscape of level fields. The towns along the lower White River and its tributaries beckoned sawmills and a fistful of woodworking factories. The town of Helena was a factory floor for lumber and wood veneer in the 1920s. It was an early booster of the dream of an industrialized New South that never came to pass.

In the 1940s and '50s, thanks to the *King Biscuit Time* radio show, Helena became the broadcast center for blues drifting across the delta. Juke joints boomed on Walnut Street, and whites secretly listened to the blues of Muddy Waters, Robert Nighthawk, and James Cotton on the radio. Then came the civil rights victories, and whites pulled their kids from integrated schools.

Now Helena-West Helena is a collapsed place—the final blow came on July 9, 1979, when Mohawk Rubber closed and took the last fat payroll with it. But there is an effort to make the town a cultural center, a shrine to the blues. Abandoned buildings say the place is over. The blues festival says it may come back. The morning light, the passing people who all say hello, the green vines that seem to devour all the work

of human beings, the Mississippi River that licks the levees—these things insist that life goes on.

THE PHOTOGRAPHER IS NOT SURE WHAT happened. Eugene Richards was at his boardinghouse. There may have been a beating, he thinks. Maybe it was because two of his black female co-workers lived in the same boardinghouse he did. The only thing he knows for sure is that he ended up with seizures, possibly from a blow to the head, and was sent to a psychiatric hospital in Texas. When he spoke to his white landlady years later, she said she had caught someone pinning Ku Klux Klan crosses to the boardinghouse's gate but hadn't wanted to worry him.

There were other incidents: his dog, Mange, shot to death; lug nuts removed from the wheels of his girlfriend's car; a gun pulled on him and some black friends at a café; his face cut by a big white man with razor blades as Richards came out of a black church one Sunday. Two young VISTA volunteers were beaten bloody with broken coffee cups in a restaurant in nearby Hughes. The assailants reportedly thought the men were Richards and a co-worker.

Responding to the abject poverty and racial

violence he'd witnessed, Richards joined with other former VISTA volunteers, including a couple from Iowa named Earl and Cherie Anthes, to start an antipoverty organization called Respect, which published a tiny newspaper, *Many Voices*. Richards began to photograph the changes taking place. He covered Klan rallies, the aftermath of race killings, black people running for office.

Now the black-and-white photographs are what remain of his time there. There is a fog over those years in Arkansas. The blow to Richards's mind left shards of recollection separated by huge gaps, little fragments that drift up without warning, such as the memory of him crossing a plowed field with Dorothea, the woman who would become his wife and whom he would photograph as she succumbed to the cancer that would kill her.

IN 1944 AT THE HOPSON PLANTATION ACROSS the Mississippi River, an innovation in agricultural practices would have far-reaching effects on the Arkansas Delta. For the first time, an entire crop was harvested using a mechanized cotton picker, thereby ushering in an era in which one machine could replace more than a hundred hands doing brutal work in the fields.

This led to a second wave of the Great Migration, an exodus in the forties and fifties and sixties of more than five million blacks escaping poverty and illiteracy and discrimination in the Arkansas and Mississippi Deltas and the rest of the South for what they hoped was the true promised land of urban life. Showing the way

was a sharecropper turned blues musician named Big Bill Broonzy, who had left Arkansas for Chicago in the 1920s and sang of his leave-taking in "Key to the Highway":

I got the key to the highway,
And I'm billed out and bound to go
I'm gonna leave here runnin'
'Cause walkin' is most too slow.

Everything here seems timeless, and yet all the changes came fast. By 1970 the sharecropping world was already disappearing, and the landscape of today—huge fields, giant machines, battered towns, few people—beginning to emerge. Today one person can farm 38,000 acres with only a dozen farmhands.

But the delta has something going for it that the rest of the nation has yet to fully learn. It is a place where race is always out on the table in plain view and is sometimes honestly discussed. A growing number of people here realize that the problems of the future won't be mastered unless race is put behind them—unless building communities with work, decent wages, and justice for all is put at the top of their agendas.

Gertrude Jackson is in her late 80s and spent her life on the delta. She'll take now over then. Especially since then was hard work with a hoe and the handcuffs of segregation: "As long as you don't have to go into the fields, it is a good day."

In the late sixties a utility pole outside her house near Marvell was shot at when she worked to end school segregation. Later she founded a community center. "When I was a kid, people didn't talk about the Elaine massacre. When civil rights people came, I heard about it." She has gray hair, wears black slacks and glasses. In her soft voice she says, "When you make up your mind to do something, you don't have any fear."

Ten of her 11 children have left—for Los Angeles, Virginia, Memphis, Baton Rouge, Georgia, the military: "There just wasn't anything here to do, so they went out." What is striking about her: She hasn't forgotten her struggle, but she seems to live in a state of grace without wounds.

Cherie Anthes and her husband, Earl, the former VISTA volunteers with whom Richards worked at the newspaper, never left the delta. She is a retired public health nurse; he still works in community development. They live in a world

Just west of the Mississippi River, the Arkansas Delta is 17 million acres of flat, fertile land laced with tributaries and dotted with towns in decline.

1969: I drove out past the town of Marion beneath a quiet sky, as beautiful as anything I'd seen, to the house of a woman who lived by herself.

they think has hit bottom, and in that fact they find hope. Earl thinks the divisions between whites and blacks, between owners and workers, don't matter anymore, because unless things get better for everyone, then it's over for everyone.

OLLY NEAL IS PART OF THE PAST AND THE future. He is 71. In the early seventies he was a firebrand, a Vietnam vet and black organizer who carried a gun in self-defense, the guy who led a boycott of white businesses in Marianna and ran a VISTA-organized health clinic there. Now most of the stores downtown are closed, the factories gone. There are only a couple of juke joints in the whole county. Neal is a retired appellate judge who once worked in the court-house in Marianna, which faces a square with a statue of Robert E. Lee.

Neal has hope. He cultivates the young, has sent a dozen locals to college. He believes they will someday return and fix the place.

Eugene Richards remembers Neal as one who inspired him but told him to leave the delta in the early seventies, said it was time for civil rights to be a black movement. It helped Richards realize his time was up. We are sitting in Neal's office when I

The delta has something going for it: Race is always out on the table in plain view and is sometimes honestly discussed.

mention this conversation. Neal snaps alert, looks over, and says, "Gene, was that you I told to go home?" and he gets up, and they embrace. Talk turns personal and emotional.

Neal and his brothers slaughter a steer each year for a barbecue. Gene must come down for this, he must. But for Richards, returning is complicated. In part because his time in Arkansas is still the burning core of his life. And in part because he left dispirited and confused about whether he'd accomplished anything at all. Now, 40 years later, the sharecropper life that he documented has slipped away. The place is less poor than it was and less rich at the same time. Whatever the South is, it stays with you, and whatever the delta is, it beats as the heart inside the South. □

FINDING WHAT ENDURES

Nobody needs to tell me that nothing stays the same. Still, what did I do when I returned to the Arkansas Delta after 40 years? What everybody does who tries to return to what was once home: search for what they knew. The first couple of days I drove maybe 500 miles looking for sharecropper shacks. There used to be hundreds of them, painted white and raised up on concrete blocks. Now there's not so much as a floorboard or a nail to mark where they were. It's as if the Mississippi had overflowed and swept them all away.

It's hard to document the disappearance of a way of life, to capture the delta that once was and isn't today. I took pictures of church services, improbably small towns, monster tractors in the fields. Early one morning I was driving past a row of abandoned workers' houses north of Lehi when I spotted a pair of women's shoes on a porch. In a Lucite box, covered in ruby red glitter, they glowed like broken glass. After taking some pictures, I hid them behind an old couch. A month later I returned with my wife, Janine. Approaching the houses, we saw six or seven men step out of a white van, each wearing fragments of military uniforms. A man who was all muscles and tattoos told us they were U.S. Special Forces and that they'd taken over the houses for military exercises. Janine asked if he'd seen the red shoes. "You mean Dorothy's shoes," he answered, clearly knowing what she was talking about. We were then told to leave.

I ask myself now what the picture of the red shoes has to do with the story of the delta, then remind myself it's only when you stop trying to make sense of things that you start seeing.

—Eugene Richards

2010: I was driving away from the cotton gin in Widener when I caught sight of an elderly woman sitting on her porch. Her name was Viola Perkins, and when I asked if I could take her picture, she smiled, either happy to have a visitor or too polite to refuse. The photograph captures her reflection in the dusty window of her house.

2010: The Peter's Rock Church in Marianna is no everlasting monument; it has been left to rot, its windows broken, its steeple fallen over. Still, I found it beautiful. Kneeling in the cemetery, listening to the insects hissing, watching as a dog wandered past, I felt history coming at me from all sides.

2010: Jeannette Kern gently smoothed back the hair of her niece, Kequsha, who looked to be in her own private world yet aware of everything going on in her aunt's tiny house in Crawfordsville. Below, a tractor created an explosion of dirt and stones as a farmer south of Marianna dug shallow trenches to ready a field for growing rice.

The rural delta is almost emptied of people as farmworkers have been replaced by machines. Few old houses remain, most having collapsed or been torn down. I encountered one, above, hidden by trees. Below, close to sunset, I followed the Kern children as they walked home, stopping to pet their dogs, seeming to dance in the shimmering heat.

NG CONNECT

Every month this page features our staff picks of National Geographic Society products and events. For more go to *nglive.org*.

NATIONAL GEOGRAPHIC ON TV

Unlikely Animal Friends

What does a warthog see in a rhino? Find out this month on the National Geographic Channel, when improbable animal relationships are the name of the game. Discover why Mtani, a young Labrador retriever, can't get enough of Kasi, a six-month-old cheetah (left, playing together at Busch Gardens in Tampa, Florida), and get to know a seal and her favorite pal: an Irish veterinarian.

BOOK	**BIRD-WATCHER'S BIBLE** If the flutter of wings has ever caught your eye, this book is for you. It's a comprehensive yet lighthearted guide to all things avian, featuring bird-watching basics, essays, the history of birds in art, and more. In stores now ($40).

EXHIBIT	**PARADISE FOUND** Eight years ago photographer Tim Laman and ornithologist Edwin Scholes set out to document every bird of paradise species. See photos and videos from their expeditions at the National Geographic Museum starting November 1. (Visit *ngmuseum.org* for info.) Their book, *Birds of Paradise,* is on sale now.

LECTURE	**ANCIENT MAYA** Archaeologist William Saturno's discoveries have illuminated the Maya calendar. Hear him speak December 3 at the Goodman Theatre in Chicago, Illinois. Go to *nglive.org* for tickets.

MAGAZINE	**INNOVATION** This edition of *Exploring History* takes on great game changers of the past, including Ben Franklin, Leonardo da Vinci, and Martin Luther King, Jr. Available November 6 wherever books and magazines are sold or online at *ngm.com/history* ($6.99).

Free Download
of the Month

Bedouin Soundclash *Light the Horizon*

On its latest album Bedouin Soundclash mines rich musical terrain. Merging Anglo rock and punk with reggae, Caribbean, and African sounds, this Canadian trio picks up where Bob Marley, the Clash, and the Police left off. For a free download from the group's album *Light the Horizon,* check out *natgeomusic.net/free.*

Shooting Stars
Capturing the flight of emperor penguins in Antarctica is no easy feat. They rocket around underwater, then explode out of holes in the sea ice (below). To follow them, Paul Nicklen used polar survival skills he learned as a child living among the Inuit on Canada's Baffin Island. He read the ice and winds, and pressed the shutter even when he lost feeling in his fingers. Every so often, penguins burst from the water at this site, where Nicklen lay waiting. "They soared underwater like fighter jets in a dogfight," he says. "Then they'd fly out, land, push down with their bill, and stand up, going back to that slow, waddling bird. It was a privilege to see." —*Luna Shyr*

BEHIND THE LENS

Penguins are pretty big. Did you worry one might hit you?

PN: I was hit once, quite hard in the head. I was in a safe place—out of their way—but a penguin went way off course, flew through the air, and landed on my head. He just casually stood up and walked away. A 70-pound bird to the head hurts a lot, but I'm lucky I've never been injured. I was also hit by a leopard seal. Its strategy is to fly out of the water and knock over penguins like bowling pins.

How close were you to the penguins in this shot?

I was about three feet away. My camera was in a [protective] Seacam housing; they were sending up so much spray and ice it would've destroyed my camera. The noises and thuds when they landed on the ice were incredible. They knocked the air out of themselves and made a squeak. We were lucky in that there was really only one opening where the penguins entered and exited the ocean.

Did you enjoy living with them?

The first night in camp, the penguins followed me home. They stood outside and bugled all night. By the third night, I had a hard time sleeping, and the romanticism began to wane.

Head in the Sand

The Sphinx, Egypt's half-beast–half-man monolith, has often been buried up to its neck. It had been dug out at least three times by the time this photo was taken. The first was around 1400 B.C. by Pharaoh Thutmose IV, again during the Roman period, and a third time beginning in 1925—the same year as this photo—by Émile Baraize, a French engineer. In the summer of 1928 *National Geographic* Editor Gilbert H. Grosvenor warned his staff not to use this image, noting on the back: "As the Sphinx has been entirely uncovered, this picture is very much out of date."

But the photo's technology wasn't. Grosvenor had installed the first color printing lab in American publishing in 1920. Photographers processed their autochrome images in the field as glass plates and shipped them via steamer to the *Geographic*'s Washington headquarters. —*Johnna Rizzo*

↖ **Flashback Archive** Find all the photos at **ngm.com.**

PHOTO: HANS HILDENBRAND, NATIONAL GEOGRAPHIC STOCK

NATIONAL GEOGRAPHIC (ISSN 0027-9358) PUBLISHED MONTHLY BY THE NATIONAL GEOGRAPHIC SOCIETY, 1145 17TH ST. NW, WASHINGTON, DC 20036. ONE YEAR MEMBERSHIP: $34.00 U.S. DELIVERY, $38.00 TO CANADA, $49.50 TO INTERNATIONAL ADDRESSES. SINGLE ISSUE: $7.00 U.S. DELIVERY, $10.00 CANADA, $15.00 INTERNATIONAL. (ALL PRICES IN U.S. FUNDS; INCLUDES SHIPPING AND HANDLING.) PERIODICALS POSTAGE PAID AT WASHINGTON, DC, AND ADDITIONAL MAILING OFFICES. POSTMASTER: SEND ADDRESS CHANGES TO NATIONAL GEOGRAPHIC, PO BOX 62130, TAMPA, FL 33662. IN CANADA, AGREEMENT NUMBER 40063649, RETURN UNDELIVERABLE ADDRESSES TO NATIONAL GEOGRAPHIC, PO BOX 4412 STN. A, TORONTO, ONTARIO M5W 3W2. UNITED KINGDOM NEWSSTAND PRICE £4.99. REPR. EN FRANCE: EMD FRANCE SA, BP 1029, 59011 LILLE CEDEX; TEL. 320.300.302; CPPAP 0715U89037; DIRECTEUR PUBLICATION: D. TASSINARI DIR. RESP. ITALY; RAPP IMD SRL, VIA G. DA VELATE 11, 20162 MILANO; AUT. TRIB. MI 258 26/5/84 POSTE ITALIANE SPA; SPED. ABB. POST. DL 353/2003 (CONV L.27/02/2004 N.46) ART 1 C. 1 DCB MILANO STAMPA QUAD/GRAPHICS, MARTINSBURG, WV 25401. MEMBERS: IF THE POSTAL SERVICE ALERTS US THAT YOUR MAGAZINE IS UNDELIVERABLE, WE HAVE NO FURTHER OBLIGATION UNLESS WE RECEIVE A CORRECTED ADDRESS WITHIN TWO YEARS.

CITY OF ADVENTURE

DURBAN
THE WARMEST PLACE TO BE

South Africa is synonymous with adventure and nowhere offers more opportunity for excitement than Durban. The area is a thrill seeker's paradise; an adrenaline junkie's dream. The action all takes place in some of the most spectacular settings imaginable—so don't forget to stop and enjoy the view!

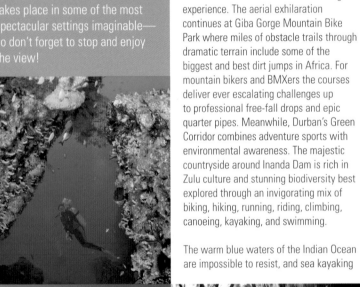

Balancing 100 meters up on the Moses Mabhida Stadium takes a lot of nerve: Jumping off takes even more! Plunging to earth at 120kph, the Big Rush Big Swing catapults you in a death-defying 220-meter arc across the stadium—a life-defining experience. The aerial exhilaration continues at Giba Gorge Mountain Bike Park where miles of obstacle trails through dramatic terrain include some of the biggest and best dirt jumps in Africa. For mountain bikers and BMXers the courses deliver ever escalating challenges up to professional free-fall drops and epic quarter pipes. Meanwhile, Durban's Green Corridor combines adventure sports with environmental awareness. The majestic countryside around Inanda Dam is rich in Zulu culture and stunning biodiversity best explored through an invigorating mix of biking, hiking, running, riding, climbing, canoeing, kayaking, and swimming.

The warm blue waters of the Indian Ocean are impossible to resist, and sea kayaking is an action-packed way to explore Durban's coastline. The sun-drenched beaches of "The Golden Mile" are at their most magnificent when seen from a kayak with a refreshing sea breeze in your face. Probably the ultimate adventure is to dive Aliwal Shoal. Rated in the top ten world dives, Aliwal Shoal has it all: wrecks, coral reefs, fish, whales, dolphins, rays, turtles, and tiger sharks. Whether you're a novice or a pro, diving Aliwal Shoal is simply one of the most exciting experiences Durban, Africa, and the world has to offer.

Find out more about adventures in Durban by visiting *www.durbanexperience.co.za*

Like us on Facebook:
Durban the warmest place to be

Images counterclockwise from top left:
Big Rush Big Swing at Moses Mabida Stadium;
diving at Aliwal Shoal off the Sapphire Coast;
board riding on Durban's beachfront;
cycling tours at Durban Green Hub;
kite surfing along the Golden Mile.